Number Activities and Games

THIRD EDITION

Compiled by
Roy Edwards
Alec Williams
Patricia Baggaley

A NASEN PUBLICATION

Published in 1993

Reprinted in 1997

ISBN 0 906730 54 6

Published by NASEN Enterprises Ltd.
NASEN Enterprises Ltd. is a company limited by guarantee, registered in England and Wales.
Company No. 2637438

Further copies of this book and details of NASEN's many other publications may be obtained from the Publications Department at its registered office:
NASEN House, 4/5 Amber Business Village, Amber Close, Amington, Tamworth, Staffs. B77 4RP.
Tel: 01827 311500; Fax: 01827 313005

Cover Design by Pam Crewe
Typeset in Plantin and printed in the United Kingdom by Harvest Printers Ltd. (Macclesfield).

Contents

Making the most of Number Activities and Games

The Games

All games relate to *National Curriculum Attainment Target 2: Number*. The range of difficulty extends from Level 1 to Level 4, with subdivisions at each Level corresponding to the respective Programmes of Study. Many of the games lend themselves to extensions both to other Attainment Targets and to higher Levels.

Where games can be adapted to two or more Levels of the National Curriculum they are classified at the lowest applicable Level. Suggestions for extensions and other variations are included in the texts.

Within each subdivision at each Level, games are graduated in an approximate order of difficulty.

Gamesheets

Preface

It was by chance that the necessity to consider a revision of *Number Activities and Games*, a best selling handbook formerly produced by the National Association for Remedial Education, coincided with the introduction of the National Curriculum in mathematics into our schools. Thus, an opportunity was provided to undertake a thorough review of the place of mathematical games within the context of teachers' present day needs. The result of these revisions bear testimony to the professionalism and integrity underlying Roy Edwards' original selection of games, based as it was on his own practical experience in the classroom and in sharing ideas with teachers on INSET courses and workshops. Magazines, newspapers, puzzle-books and even Christmas crackers were other sources quoted by Roy but, common to all, was the criteria of practical usage and evaluation. Whilst a few activities were openly designated as useful five-minute time-fillers, the vast majority were conceived within a clearly defined curricular context, widening and consolidating learned skills and concepts offering both interest and challenge.

It thus occasioned little surprise that with very few exceptions, the games and activities could easily be classified within the all-important National Curriculum 'Number' New Attainment Target, primarily within Levels 2 to 4. Within each Level, selected Programmes of Study were found to provide the necessary basis for a more specific differentiation that would enable teachers to identify games to meet individual mathematical needs. The next logical step was to plan for the inclusion in the revision of a number of new games within the Programmes of Study of Level 1, thus providing the teacher with supporting games and activities ranging from the earliest development levels (at whatever age), to the stage of mastery of the four basic processes following the introduction of place-value.

A further consideration was the development in mathematics teaching of the use of computers and calculators. Though the use of computer games can satisfy similar criteria to those included in *Number Activities and Games*, questions of access, compatibility and continual updating would suggest a separate publication is necessary to do justice to developments in this area. However, calculators have a significant and permanent part to play, both in games designed to exploit their potentialities and as a checking device in games not specifically designed for their use.

In summary, this Revised Edition of *Number Activities and Games* is characterised by:

1. A wide selection of games from the 2nd Edition, with content updated where appropriate.

2. The introduction of newly selected games at National Curriculum Level 1, each satisfying the original criterion of 'workability' within the classroom.

3. The retention of clearly defined curricular objectives for each game.

4. The classification of all items under Levels 1 to 4 of National Curriculum New Attainment Target No. 2 and within Programmes of Study subdivisions.

5. The introduction of calculator games with advice on the place and usage of the calculator in mathematical games.

An undoubted benefit of the National Curriculum has been the emphasis accorded to developmental stages of progression and the corresponding need for differentiation in the strategies required for their realisation. Thus the new range and format of *Number Activities and Games* will be of particular use with pupils with learning difficulties, combining the advantage of activities offering reinforcement and consolidation with the assurance that the challenge provided will be at a level commensurate with the pupil's abilities and potential.

The NASEN Publications Sub-Committee has warmly welcomed the opportunity to publish this revised edition of *Number Activities and Games*. As with previous editions, comments and suggestions based on the use of the games in the classroom will be welcomed and carefully considered.

Making the most of this Handbook

Why we use Games

Games in mathematics teaching have undergone a change in status. Notions of their use as five-minute time-fillers, for Friday afternoons and rainy games periods have given way to their acceptance as a planned and valuable means of achieving and consolidating curricular objectives in ways which can be enjoyable, challenging and rewarding. Games not only satisfy the need for practice and reinforcement of new learning but also provide significant opportunities for the generalisation and transfer that ensure its usability in a variety of contexts.

Particularly for children with learning difficulties, the false security of merely repetitive learning can be replaced by active responses generated by playing selected games at an appropriate level of challenge. Interpreting, discussing and following rules, making decisions and devising scoring systems provide a social context that enhances motivation and generates positive attitudes towards mathematics at these early, formative stages. To learn to win and lose, to take turns, to experience tension and to continue in the face of difficulties can contribute towards personal and social maturity — an excellent foundation for the more challenging open—ended mathematical challenges that lie ahead.

Using Calculators with Mathematical Games

'Pupils should have the opportunity to explore the way a calculator works through a variety of number games and similar activities'.

National Curriculum Council
Mathematics: Non-statutory Guidance.

The calculator is thus one item in a range of apparatus to which pupils should have access if they are to be encouraged and helped to develop their own methods for doing calculations. A balanced curriculum is likely to include the use of a calculator, devising strategies for mental calculations or resorting to the use of pencil and paper. In the National Curriculum, some Statements of Attainment specify the use of a calculator whilst others exclude its use.

Calculators are not meant to be replacements for, but rather supplements to, other methods. They can be used both as a means of acquiring mathematical knowledge and as a tool for calculating or checking answers following computation. Using the calculator, mathematical concepts can be reinforced, extended or new concepts introduced (e.g. inverse and other relationships between the four basic processes.) In the formative stages of number development covered by this book, the foundations of flexible mental calculations are mostly the addition and multiplication number bonds within the context of a sound grasp of place-value.

With the speed, accuracy and ease of use of calculators, motivation is increased, allowing pupils to focus on the meaning of their results and how to use them rather than concentrating on the mechanics of the operation. Problem solving involving realistic data is possible without the anxiety of dealing with large numbers. Instant answers enable predictions to be made and tested easily, thus encouraging discovery of possible strategies towards a solution. Of particular value are the opportunities provided by the calculator for a speedy check on approximations and estimations in assessing their reasonableness in the context of the problem.

In *Number Activities and Games* those games which have been specifically designed for the use of a calculator are indicated alongside the game numbers by a calculator. Once introduced, the calculator may be used for checking purposes for most of the remaining games at Levels 3 and 4.

Making the Games

The purchase of even a small number of games in ready-made 'kit' form can be prohibitively expensive. Within the very considerable economies effected by introducing a large number of games in book format, their presentation in *Number Activities and Games* has been planned to make the least possible demands on teachers' time by presenting as much as possible of the material to be used by the pupils in a form that can be photocopied.

Where use of the photocopier is recommended, this is indicated alongside the title of the game at the top of the page:

 indicates that the diagram/illustration on that page can be copied. Normally, that part of the text addressed to the teacher should be masked.

Gamesheet, accompanied by a number, indicates that a separate sheet, essential to the game and intended for photocopying, can be found at the back of the book. *Gamesheets* take two forms. They are either intended to be photocopied as worksheets or, pasted on to some form of card cut out according to the requirements of the game. Materials that can be re-used many times — such as Gamesheet 4 - should be covered with clear plastic film.

For those games where either the size or the nature of the materials required precludes the use of the photocopier, the teacher can often exploit the situation by engaging pupils in the tasks of designing, measuring, estimating, controlling and economising in the selection of materials and precision in execution.

For all games, teachers will need to have available basic materials such as pencils, crayons, paper, counters, dice etc., as indicated in the 'materials' section. See overleaf (vi), for advice on storage of games and its effect on classroom organisation.

The needs of individual pupils can be met by adapting an activity or game to:

— other mathematical skills and concepts than those specified.
— other levels of difficulty as the age and ability of each pupil requires.
— modification of time limits, where applicable.

Practicalities in using the Games

i. The careful grading and classification of the games enables the teacher to achieve a balance, avoiding both non-demanding success and the frustration of failure. Check that the pupil has the necessary pre-requisite skills to have a reasonable chance of success at the level selected.

ii. Don't give the whole class a new activity all at once. Select a small group for a start whilst others are occupied with well-established practices until it is their turn.

iii. Don't over-use games. Use strategically for consolidation, variety, revision and back-up.

iv. Check that *you* understand the activity involved in a newly introduced game and that you have either tried it yourself or witnessed its use. Become familiar with both the strong and the weaker points of the game before you introduce it.

v. Don't regard the advice under the 'Number of Participants' heading as absolute. You know your pupils and you should lose no opportunities to permit and encourage discussion in pairs and groups, even with games designated for individual play. It is good practice to draw a group together from those who have been working alone on an activity, both to consolidate the learning and to explore possibilities for extensions.

vi. The provision of suitable packaging for individual games and arrangements for systematic storage with easy and understandable access for pupils is an essential preliminary to making use of mathematical games. Time spent in the first instance in ensuring that pupils fully understand their responsibilities in relation to re-packing *all* the pieces and correctly replacing the game within the storage system is well rewarded in the achievement of a smoothly running operation.

Paired-Mathematics - Peer and Parent Involvement in Games

The success of paired-reading schemes throughout the country has prompted many schools to initiate parallel projects in mathematics, involving either parents or peers and making use of mathematical games. Most schemes incorporate the following principles:

i. Pairing can be with parents, volunteer adults or peers.

ii. Games, both manufactured and school-made, form the basis of activities.

iii. Projects are launched with an initial briefing of the adults or peers involved, often incorporating a workshop element.

iv. Subsequent training can be by means of
   — further sessions held in school,
   — teacher visiting homes,
   — use of training booklets.

v. Plan for feedback from adult/peer using simple documentation.

vi. Most schemes permit pupils' choice in games, though guidance must be available to avoid pupil-game mismatch.

vii. Time spent on games should be subject to control. Many useful mathematical games can extend well beyond typical paired-reading session times.

Most reports are of high levels of motivation of participating pupils with substantial carry-over benefits to mathematics in schools. Discretion is necessary as to the length of paired-mathematics projects — better a shorter period where the dynamic is maintained than to risk a tailing-off through a scheme that has become over-demanding of time and resources.

Many of the games in *Number Activities and Games* are ideally suited for use in paired-mathematics schemes.

Methods of Keeping Score

Many of the games require scores to be kept as the game progresses. For younger and less-able pupils, comparison of scores can be a valuable mathematical activity in its own right with particular reference to the language of difference — same, more etc — and the extent of the difference — two more, one less etc.

Gates.
If pencil and paper is used for scoring, encourage the use of 'gates' to facilitate comparison.

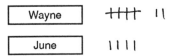

| Wayne | ┼┼┼┼ ⵏ |
| June | ⵏⵏⵏⵏ |

The double track.
Make a simple double track to use with counters and name cards.

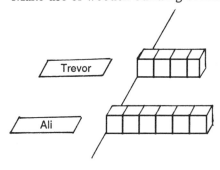

Blocks.
Make use of wooden building bricks, Unifix or Multilink cubes.

Threaded beads.
Make use of beads (of identical size) on threading cords.

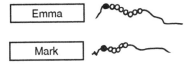

Level 1

Understanding the language of number
Understanding conservation of number

Games in this section relate to cardinal groupings only. Activities relating to other aspects of conservation such as volume, area and weight offer additional enrichment in concept formation at this stage, particularly when emphasing the use of comparative terms (more, same, longer, enough etc).

Throughout this section, reference is made to 'dot' patterns. In order to achieve generalisation, the instruction should be interpreted very liberally to include configurations of shapes (stars, triangles etc) as well as easily identifiable mini-patterns of everyday objects.

Game 1   Paired

Objective: To familiarise pupils with varieties of dot patterns that make up a number. To help develop concentration and memorisation.

Number of participants: Two to four players.

Materials: i.   A stiff card measuring 36cm × 36cm divided into 6cm × 6cm squares. The squares are filled by a random distribution of dot patterns representing 6 variations of each number from 3 to 8.

      ii.   36 'cover' cards measuring 6cm × 6cm.

      iii.   36 'paired' cards measuring 6cm × 6cm in a contrasting colour.

Procedure: i.   A 'cover' card is placed over all 36 patterns by an adult or a pupil not involved in the game.

      ii.   The first player lifts any 'cover' card to expose a pattern.

      iii.   The same player lifts a second 'cover' card to expose its pattern. If the patterns have the same value the player claims both the 'cover' cards and the two patterns are covered by a 'paired' card. If the patterns have a different value, the 'cover' cards are replaced.

      iv.   The second or next player repeats stages ii and iii.

      v.   Play continues until all patterns have been paired. The winner is the player who has accumulated most 'cover' cards.

This is an excellent game for developing concentration. Memorising the value of the patterns that have been re-covered by the cover card gives players a considerable advantage. Games tend to start slowly (1 chance in 6 of patterns having the same value) but speeds up considerably as players remember the value of the decreasing number of unpaired patterns.

Game 2   Scatter

Objective: To familiarise pupils with varieties of dot patterns that make up a number. To provide opportunities to make use of a comparative vocabulary (more, same, less etc).

Number of participants: Up to eight pupils.

Materials: i.   A large number of 8cm × 8cm cards with differing dot configurations (small sticky-backed shapes or marker blobs) representing each number from 2 to 9. Allow a total of approximately 16 cards for each participant.

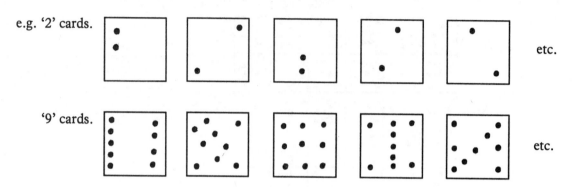

e.g. '2' cards.   etc.

'9' cards.   etc.

         ii.   A scoring chart with space for (changeable) name cards (of sufficient size to accommodate the pairs of cards).

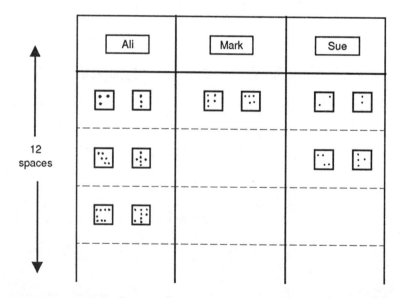

Procedure: Cards are scattered at random, face upwards, over any large floor area (playground, school hall etc). On word 'go' each pupil moves amongst the cards seeking pairs having the same number of dots. The cards are picked up and placed alongside each other on the scoring chart. Pupils check the accuracy of each others pairs at the conclusion of the game when all the cards have been picked up. The winner, of course, is the pupil with the most correct pairings.

Practice at this type of game greatly improves pupils' ability to estimate the value of the cards, which should be encouraged.

Game 3   Beggar my neighbour

Objective: To familiarise pupils with variations in number patterns from 2 to 8. To provide practice to determine the larger (or smaller) of two such patterns.

Number of participants: Two.

Materials: Six cards (8cm × 8cm) representing each number from 2 to 8 in differing dot patterns, making 42 cards in all. (A selection from the cards produced for **Scatter**, Game 2 would be suitable.)

Procedure:

   i.   The cards are shuffled and divided evenly between the two players, face downwards.

   ii.   First player turns top card over and places it at the side of his/her pack.

   iii.   Second player does likewise. Player with the largest value card takes both cards and places them at the bottom of his/her pack. If the cards have the same value, both are put into a 'pool' and can be claimed by the player winning the next turn. Cards should be periodically shuffled.

Variation: A 'misére' version. The player with the smallest value card takes both cards.

Game 4   Pattern snap

Objective: As **Beggar my Neighbour** (Game 3).

Number of participants: Two or three.

Materials:

   i.   Eight cards (8cm × 8cm) representing each number from 2 to 8 in differing dot patterns, making 56 cards in all. (A selection of the cards produced for **Scatter**, Game 2, page 12 would be suitable).

   ii.   Counters for scoring.

Procedure: Each player starts with 5 counters.

   i.   The pack is shuffled and piled face downwards between the players. The top card is placed face upwards at the side.

   ii.   The first player turns next card over and places it face upwards at the side of the other exposed card.

   iii.   If cards have the same value, the player to call 'Snap' first checks his or her call by counting the dots out loud on both cards. If call is correct, the caller claims one counter from the bank. If call is incorrect, the caller must pay a counter into the bank.

The winner is the player with most counters when the pack is exhausted.

Game 5   Same but different

Objective: To familiarise pupils with varieties of dot patterns that make up a number. To help develop concentration and memorisation.

Number of participants: Two to four players.

Materials: Five cards (8cm × 8cm) representing each number from 3 to 8 in differing dot patterns. (A selection from the cards produced for **Scatter**, Game 2 would be suitable).

Procedure:

i.   Cards are shuffled and scattered face down on floor or table.

ii.   First player turns over a 'stimulus' card.

iii.   The same player turns over a second card. If the cards have the same value, the player claims both cards and one point. If the cards have a different value, both are replaced face-down in their original position.

iv.   Continue until all cards have been paired. The player with the most (correct) pairs is the winner. (The scoring chart used for **Scatter** Game 2 may be used).

This is an excellent game for developing concentration. Memorising the value of the cards that have been turned over and replaced gives players a considerable advantage. Games tend to start slowly (1 chance in 6 of cards having same value) but speeds up considerably as pupils remember the value of the cards that have been exposed.

Please note: It has been indicated that the cards for the five games involving cardinal correspondence (pages 11 - 14) can utilise the same 'dot' cards originally made for **Scatter**. Whilst this has obvious practical advantages it must be stressed, in order to achieve generalisation, that pupils should have access to cards with presentational differences in relation to size, colour, pattern configuration and changes in the dots/shapes used to represent each number.

Game 6　　　　In the bag

Objective:　　Estimation of an unseen but handled number of items from 4 to 10 with confirmatory counting.

Number of participants: Two.

Materials:　　Cotton bag, 25cm × 15cm, with drawstring. Sets of ten items of varying size but sufficiently small for all items to be contained in the bag.

Procedure:　　i.　Working with hands below table level, first player puts between 4 and 10 items from one set into bag and pulls the drawstring.

　　　　　　ii.　Second player handles the bag in any way he/she pleases and estimates number of items contained.

　　　　　　iii.　Bag is opened and both players agree on contents by counting. Where appropriate, 2 points may be awarded for a correct estimate and 1 point for an estimate which is one out either way. Otherwise, count 1 point for a correct estimate.

Different sets of items to be used in successive games.

Game 7   Skittles

Objective: Achieving 1 - 1 correspondence between counting and the size of a set. Providing opportunities for use of language of comparison e.g. "I've got 2 more", "How many have you got altogether?" etc.

Number of participants: Two, three or four.

Materials: Ninepins (plastic for use indoors because of noise) and ball.

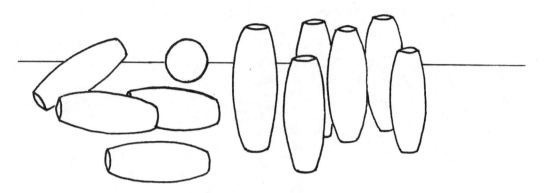

    i.   Ten Unifix, Multilink or small cubic bricks for each player.

   ii.   Name card for each player to be used on scoring chart:

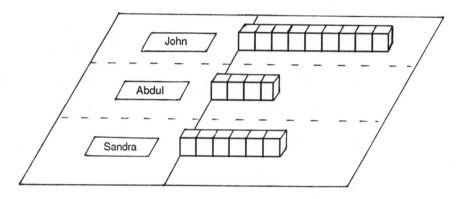

Procedure: Skittles is best played in a hall, along a corridor or outside.

Players take it in turn to bowl. For every pin knocked down one brick or item is placed on the scoring chart. The first player to use all his/her scoring items is the winner.

If practice in counting above 10 is desirable, more scoring items are made available. Another progression is to introduce an addition element by having different values for each skittle, according to colour or label.

Game 8   Dotty dominoes

Objective: To familiarise pupils with the equivalence of varying dot patterns of numbers 3 - 8.

Number of participants: Two, three or four players.

Materials: 36 dominoes on stiff card, each 8cm × 4cm, marked domino style but with varying configurations of patterns from 3 to 8.

e.g.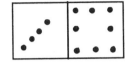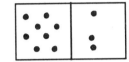

The set will comprise:

3 - 3	4 - 3	5 - 3	6 - 3	7 - 3	8 - 3
3 - 4	4 - 4	5 - 4	6 - 4	7 - 4	8 - 4
3 - 5	4 - 5	5 - 5	6 - 5	7 - 5	8 - 5
3 - 6	4 - 6	5 - 6	6 - 6	7 - 6	8 - 6
3 - 7	4 - 7	5 - 7	6 - 7	7 - 7	8 - 7
3 - 8	4 - 8	5 - 8	6 - 8	7 - 8	8 - 8

Also counters for scoring.

Procedure:

i.   Whole domino pack is shuffled and put into pile, face down.

ii.   Top domino is placed face upwards on table.

iii.   First player takes next domino from pile and attempts to match with upturned domino. If successful, places domino usual fashion and picks up counter to indicate 1 point. If unsuccessful, puts domino face down on a discard pile.

iv.   Players continue either until the pack is exhausted or by shuffling the discard pile at the stage and continuing to play until all dominoes have been placed. Determine which alternative before the commencement of play.

Variation: Count 2 points for being able to play a 'double' domino.

Game 9   Counting to carry

Objective: Counting and memorising the number of items in a set of up to 15 items in order to carry out a subsequent operation involving that number.

Number of participants: Two.

Materials: 4 cards, 8cm × 8cm, for each number from 1 to 15; each with varying dot patterns. Cards to be sorted into three sets, 1 to 5, 6 to 10 and 11 to 15, each set in a distinctive colour.

15 counters in container.

Two or three sets of 20 items (shells, buttons, coins etc.) each in separate container.

Simple counting board for checking correspondence between sets.

1st set (counters)

Distant set (shells)

Procedure: Teacher determines which of the three sets of cards is most appropriate, according to stage of development of players.

      i.   Chosen set of cards is shuffled and placed face downwards. First player turns over top card.

      ii.   Same pupil counts number of dots on card, takes that number of counters and places them (as above) on one side of counting board.

      iii.   Same pupil goes to the other set of items which is either at the other side of the room (or perhaps outside the room) and *in one journey only* brings back the appropriate number of items.

      iv.   Pupil places items from distant set on other side of counting board. Both players agree on correspondence.

      v.   The first player to reach an agreed number of scores is the winner, each player having had an identical number of turns.

Note: Many pupils, though able to count with accuracy, appear to have difficulty in using that skill in applied situations. In this game, the greater the distance between the two sets, the less likelihood that correspondence is being achieved through any form of visual matching rather than through memorisation and counting.

Ensure generalisation through changing the items in the 'carrying' set.

Game 10 More counting to carry

Objective: As **Counting to Carry**, Game 9 but with introduction of concepts of "1 more" and "1 less" introduced into the operation.

Number of participants: Two.

Materials: As **Counting to Carry** with the addition of a set of 12 'process' cards, 6 with the message '1 more' and 6 with '1 less'.

Procedure: The 12 'process' cards are shuffled and placed in a pile face downwards alongside the other cards.

The procedure for **Counting to Carry** is followed except that at the end of stage 2, the player takes the top 'process' card. He/she must then carry over 1 more or 1 less than the number of counters according to the instructions on the process card. This is taken into account when the items on the counting board are checked and agreed.

Note: For some pupils this game represents a significant advance in understanding both in reinforcing the notion that the size of a set is represented by the last number in the count but also that the preceding and succeeding numbers, represent 1 less and 1 more respectively. In particular, some pupils with specific learning difficulties will need careful and systematic guidance with this operation.

Game 11   Number boards

Objective: Relating numerals 1 to 9 with corresponding patterns representing their cardinal value.

Number of participants: One.

Materials: A board (thick cardboard or hardboard) as illustrated (33cm × 25cm) with nine squares (7cm × 7cm) cut from it. The numerals are drawn on the resulting 7cm² tiles which are then cut into the number of pieces represented by the numeral. The pattern of these cuts can vary with the perceptual skills of the children. For instance, it might be unwise to divide the figure 4 as it is shown in the illustration. If such a difficulty presents itself try to eliminate it because it will distract from the main teaching objective which here is the fourness of 4.

The board should be backed by a further layer of card to stop the tiles falling through when the board is lifted.

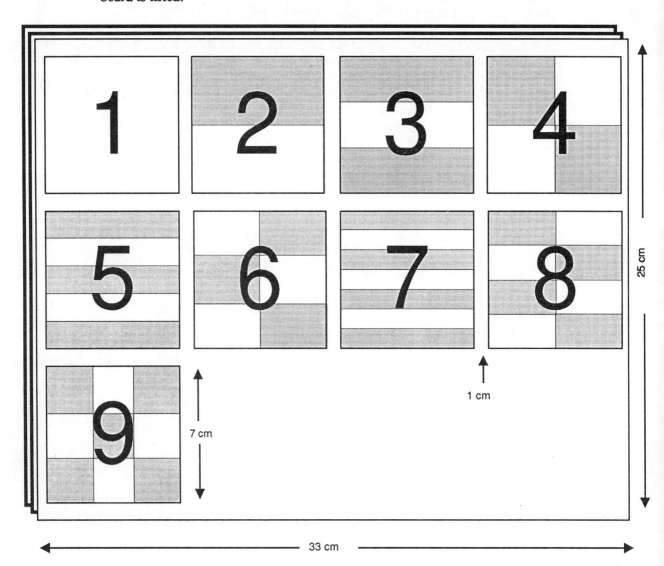

The appropriate numeral may be inscribed in each inset.

Each numeral may be drawn on differently coloured card or, more economically perhaps, drawn in a different colour. This will make the task easier than is illustrated - in black and white only.

Procedure: The fragmented numeral tiles are presented one at a time to the child to fit into the board in order (ordinal number). The teacher says the number and encourages the child to repeat it as he/she slots in the pieces. He/She may count the pieces as he/she assembles them.

Later the numerals are presented randomly.

(2) A variation of the same kind of task with the same objective: the cardination of numbers 1 to 9.

Number of participants: One or a group depending on supplies.

Materials: Nine thin cards about A4 size (29cm × 21cm) on which the numeral to be practised is written boldly and large at the top; a set of nine cards per child; a supply of photographs and pictures preferably of real things collected from magazines. Have a 'one' box, a 'two' box, a 'three' box and so on.

Procedure: The children select appropriate pictures and paste them on the card one by one to produce a collection of 'one' pictures, of 'two' pictures and so on. Their reading sight vocabulary can be enhanced by the teacher printing labels on the pictures: e.g. 'two rabbits', 'two men', 'two buses' or whatever.

Game 12   Sets of numbers

Objective: Relating numerals 2 to 9 with corresponding patterns representing their cardinal value.

Number of participants: Four or two (taking two numbers each).

Materials: Game 1: Four master cards each marked with a numeral 2, 3, 4 or 5; seven cards for each master card with a picture of the required number of objects. Real life photos are preferred, but drawings of real objects will do.

Look for suitable pictures in magazines. (The cards need not all be exactly the same size). The puzzle becomes a little more difficult perceptually if, for example, a row of four houses is shown, or four cars in a car park.

Procedure: Shuffle the four master cards. Place them face down on the table. Each player in turn takes one and places it face up on his/her left.
Shuffle the picture cards and place in a pile face down in the middle of the table.
One is turned over and the child with that number takes the card and places alongside the master card. The next child takes a picture card and places it face up and the player with the appropriate master card claims the picture, and so on.
The first to get all seven cards wins.

Stage 2: Use more abstract shapes or symbols for the picture cards, e.g. dots, circles, triangles.

Stage 3: Extend the cardinal numbers by using a new set of cards for 6, 7, 8 and 9.

For the youngest and/or least able children fewer than seven cards may be appropriate.

Game 13   Spin a number I

Objective: To match numerals from 1 to 9 with a corresponding cardinal group.

Number of participants: Two if each player takes two quarters of the board.
                                     Four if each takes a quarter of the board.

Materials: A board (hardboard or thick cardboard) as illustrated 44cm × 44cm. The pointer can be fixed to a plastic washer (a counter drilled through its centre does well) and fastened to spin freely and balanced with a large brass paper fastener. Each quarter of the board to be coloured blue, red, green and yellow respectively.

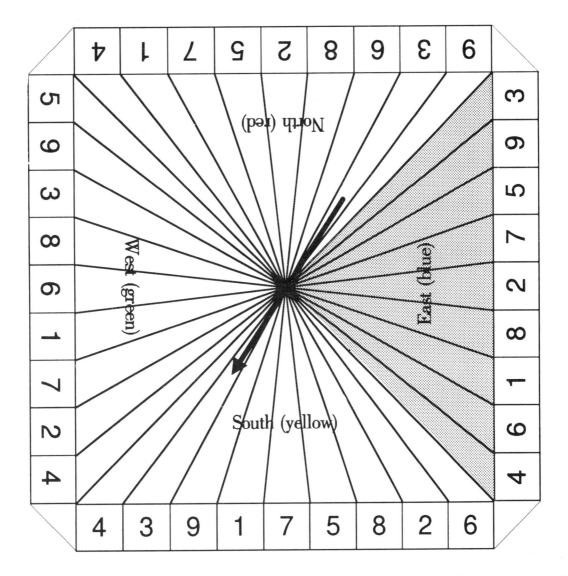

A set of cards, dot patterned 1 to 9 (ordered or jumbled according to pupil's ability), for each quarter in the appropriate colour. Second and third sets of cards with item and pattern variations will assist generalisation.

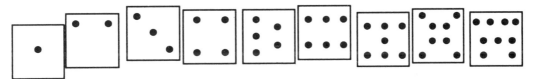

Procedure: Each player has his/her tiles spread out near his/her quarter of the board. The pointer is spun. When it comes to rest the player in whose quarter it points places the appropriate card over the matching numeral.
                     The winner is the first to place all of his or her cards correctly.

Game 14   Find the same

Objective: To develop the ability to match numerals from 3 to 9 with varied, corresponding dot patterns. The form of the game calls for concentration and memorisation.

Number of participants: Two, three or four.

Materials: Prepare six cards, 8cm × 8cm, for each number from 3 to 9, 3 of the cards bearing the numeral and 3 bearing varied dot patterns.

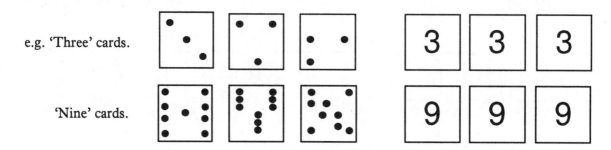

e.g. 'Three' cards.

'Nine' cards.

Procedure:

i.   The cards are shuffled and scattered randomly between the players.

ii.   The first player turns over two cards. If they correspond (symbol-symbol, pattern-pattern, symbol-pattern) both are claimed by the player. If they do not correspond both cards are replaced face-down, in their original position, by the player.

iii.   Players take alternative turns. Players remembering the value of cards already exposed and replaced are at an obvious advantage.

iv.   Continue until all cards have been paired and claimed.
The winner is the player with the most claimed cards.

Note: For pupils at the early stages of symbolisation, cards representing the higher numbers can be withdrawn and introduced selectively as ability and confidence increases.

This form of game with its demands on concentration and memorisation is an excellent basis for a wide range of games involving correspondence, at any mathematical level.

Game 15   Pass the message

Objective: To establish pupils' ability to write and interpret number symbols in a practical situation.

Number of participants: Two.

Materials: A movable screen 50cm wide × 40cm high.
20 matchboxes or 20 building bricks, approx 25mm cubed.
Pencil and small slips of paper for each player.

Procedure: Players sit facing each other with screen between them.
Each player has 10 matchboxes/bricks.

    i.   First player decides on number between 0 and 9 and makes a pile of that number of matchboxes/bricks.

    ii.   First player writes the numeral on slip of paper and passes paper round screen to second player.

    iii.   Second player makes a pile of matchboxes/bricks to correspond with number on paper.

    iv.   Screen is lifted to compare number of items in each pile.

    v.   Repeat stage i to iv with players taking opposite roles. The game continues until one player reaches a previously agreed score, with both having had an equal number of turns.

Note: Teachers may wish for the pupils to have the words 'boxes' or 'bricks' to copy so that the message reads '6 boxes'.

The technique of passing messages in this way has many uses at more advanced levels. It is particularly applicable at the appropriate stage in providing practice in writing and using the symbols for the four basic processes, e.g. 3 + 5 bricks. Here, in contrast to simple enumeration, the +, -, × and ÷ signs represent *actions* to be carried out.

Game 16   Hanging to dry   Gamesheet 2

Objective: A practical activity introducing simple serial correspondence.
Opportunities for use of ordinal terms (next to, first, between etc.) in a co-operative situation.

Number of participants: Two.

Materials: Two clothes lines and posts. Lines approx 50 cm long.
Two identical sets of 7 different clothing items, cut from cloth or paper.
Paper clips for clothes pegs.

Procedure: i.   First player hangs clothes on line in any preferred order.

            ii.   Second player is required to:
       — to copy the first line on to the second line
       — (if room) to continue the sequence on the first line
       — to reverse the order of items on the second line
       — repeat the above, starting with an item other than at either end of the sequence.

Note: For this activity dispense with winners and losers. The criteria for its success will be the degree of co-operation and the quality and amount of mathematical language generated.

Initial attempts should be made with an odd number of items, thus ensuring the matching of the centre items when the sequence is to be reversed.

Game 17   Time for bed

Objective: A game to develop understanding of ordinal correspondence, with particular emphasis on use of comparative terms relating to size.

Number of participants: Two.

Materials: No sophistication is necessary with regard to the materials.
The only essential is that a true proportion is achieved in the size of all the items.

i.   5 rag dolls of descending size, the tallest 25 — 30cm.

ii.   5 wooden beds of descending size, the largest approximately 30 cm long.

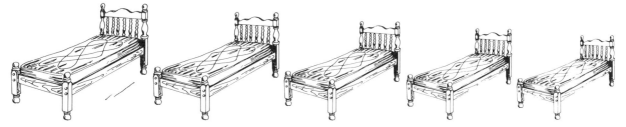

iii.   5 bedsheets of an appropriate size. A second set (in a contrasting colour) generates significant additional dialogue.

iv.   5 pillows of appropriate sizes.

Procedure: 'Put each of the dolls to bed. Look at the size of the dolls and at the size of the beds carefully.'

Repeat the instruction for the sheets (one or two sets) and for the pillows.

Notes on **Time for Bed!**
Enlist the help of co-operative parents to make the materials for this activity. The mathematical value of the game and the pleasure the pupils derive from it fully justify the trouble taken.

An understanding of ordinal (serial) correspondence, though much neglected in schools, has much significance for future mathematical development. For example, the use of structural materials (Cuisenaire, Multilink) can only have full meaning if the pupil understands the relationship between the cardinal value of the particular rod — the number of units it represents — and its place in the order of the 'stair' formed by the rods.

Time for Bed, as presented, would be unrealistically difficult for pupils without some previous experience at the more elemental stages of this form of matching. Where necessary, experience may need to start with *larger* and *smaller* items being placed *next to* each other. Subsequently with the introduction of another item in the series, concepts of *first, second, third,* and *between* arise. Only then can the relationship with a corresponding series be introduced, probably initially with just two items in each series.

The materials introduced by **Time for Bed** are of course adaptable to be used selectively in this way. Most of the stages of progression are best introduced by the teacher placing one of the series in correct order. At more advanced levels progressions can include increasing the number of items in each series, increasing the number of series to be matched and, of course, commencing the activity by having all items jumbled up.

Variations: Try any corresponding series from real life:

— footballs and footballers;

— bells and clappers;

— donkeys and tails;

— houses, windows and doors.

Game 18   Along the line

Objective: To emphasise the serial value of numbers from 1 to 9.

Number of participants: Two.

Materials: Stiff card 72cm × 8cm divided into 9 sections. No other markings.

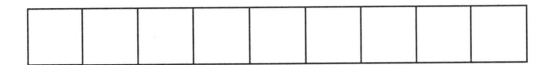

9 cards, 8cm × 8cm, in each of three colours.
Cards to have different dot configurations for each number from 1 to 9. One counter (as marker).

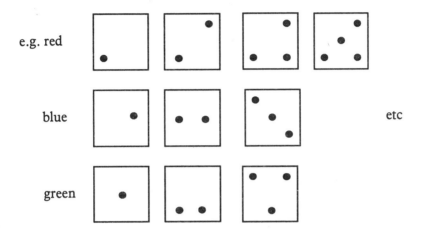

Procedure: The 9 cards of one colour are shuffled and placed in a pile, face-downwards on the table.

     i.   First player picks up top card and places it face upwards on the table.

     ii.   First player places marker on the square on the number line estimated to represent the serial value of the upturned card. Thus the 5-dot card would be represented by the marker on the fifth square from the left.

     iii.   The player checks the accuracy of his/her estimate by counting out loud by touch the dots on the card and then counting out loud by touch the number of squares from the start of the number line. The second player checks the accuracy.

     iv.   The 'used' card is replaced in the pack and the pack reshuffled after each turn. A correct estimate is rewarded by one point.

     v.   The second player repeats stage i to iv. The game then continues until one player reaches a previously agreed score (having ensured that players have had a similar number of turns.)

Note: In the case of pupils experiencing difficulty, at stage iii. Each item on the upturned card can be covered with a counter. The counters can then be placed one in each space on the number line.

If it is considered that players would benefit from further practice, subsequent games should be played with cards of a different colour.

Game 19   Number Series I   Gamesheet 3

Objective: To order randomly presented numerals from 1 to 9.

Number of participants: One, or several working separately.

Materials: Sheets of numerals as given below.

Procedure: Players follow instructions given in frames.

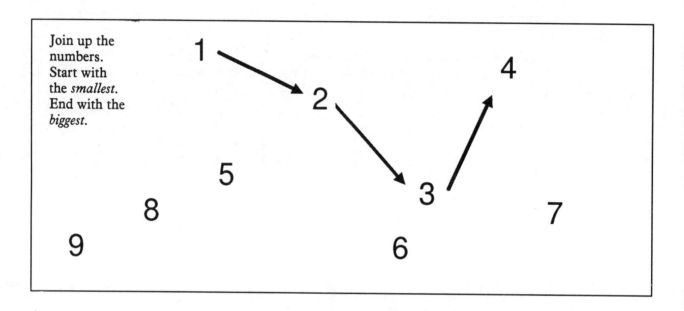

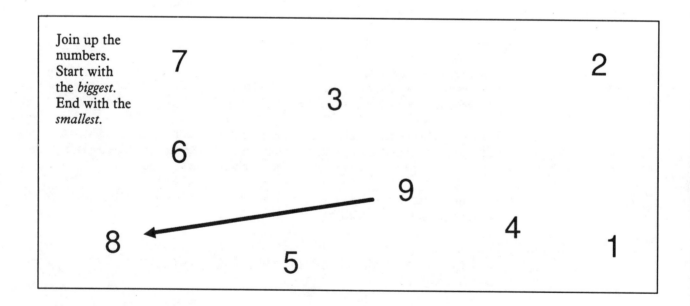

Note: Other variations include:
- joining odd (or even) numbers.
- including two numerals for each number from 1 to 8 and one number 9. Players must then find a route from 1 to 9 and then return by the alternative route.

30

Game 20   What's the number?

Objective: To reinforce knowledge of the sequence of numerals 0 to 9.

Number of participants: Two.

Materials: Ten cards of any convenient size numbered 0 to 9.

Procedure:

i.   The shuffled cards are scattered face downwards.

ii.   The first player picks up a card, putting it to one side without looking at the face side.

iii.   The same player must identify the chosen card by turning over and ordering the remaining cards.

iv.   The second player repeats stage i to iii and game continues until one player reaches an agreed score with both having had an equal number of turns.

Note: At the early stages of the introduction to place-value, the game can be played with the addition of cards from 10 to 19.

Another variation at the pre-symbolic stage is the use of dot patterns in place of numerals.

Game 21   Got It! I

Objective: To identify a number from 0 to 9 through questioning.

Number of participants: Two.

Materials: 20 cards of any convenient size; 2 of each number from 0 to 9.

Procedure: First player shuffles cards and places them in a pile, face downwards.

i.   First player takes top card, memorises number, and places card face downwards at side of pack.

ii.   Second player asks questions to determine number on card whilst first player keeps frequency count of number of questions asked. The 'gate' technique is recommended. Questions can only be answered by 'yes' or 'no'.

iii.   Change roles after number has been determined.
        The winner of each 'heat' (i.e. after each has had a turn) scores 1 point.

iv.   The winner is the one with the larger number of points when the card pile is exhausted.

Note: There is little or no point in continuing to play **Got It!** if questioning remains entirely random. Though over-tuition would be counter productive, insights into notation can be fostered by some assistance in developing a strategy to eliminate unwanted numbers, thus narrowing the range of choice. The development of such a strategy is a necessary preliminary to the more sophisticated skills required for **Got It!** (II) (Game 38).

Level 2

Knowing and using addition and subtraction facts to ten.
It should be noted that one National Curriculum Programme of Study at Level 1 calls for 'Addition and subtraction with numbers no greater than ten *in the context of real objects*'. It is emphasised that the games provided at Level 2 are not a substitute for mathematics derived from, or used in, reality situations and should be preceded by ample practical experience in accordance with the above statement.

Reading, writing and ordering number to 10.
Reference should be made to the notes on the teaching of place value, pp. 125-6.

Using coins in simple contexts.
In **Chance**, the first game, single denomination coins are used as counters. **Pay up!** and **Making Money** require an understanding of equivalence of coin values. With younger children, or those with learning difficulties, mastery of equivalence may only be achieved in carefully graduated stages, maybe starting with one or two pence coins only with a later controlled introduction of the larger denominations.

Game 22　　Matching pairs

Objectives:　To practise addition to 10 (very occasionally to 11) by:
　　　　　Stage 1　Using dot patterns.
　　　　　Stage 2　Using dots and numerals.
　　　　　Stage 3　Using numerals only.

Number of participants: Up to four players, plus a referee who could be an able child.

Materials:　A series of 34 cards (playing card size: 90mm × 65mm) or, for the first game, dominoes marked with these numbers of dots:

	2 1	3 1	4 1	5 1	6 1
1 2	2 2	3 2	4 2	5 2	6 2
1 3	2 3	3 3	4 3	5 3	6 3
1 4	2 4	3 4	4 4	5 4	6 4
1 5	2 5	3 5	4 5	5 5	6 5
1 6	2 6	3 6	4 6	5 6	

Perhaps a calculator or an abacus for the referee to check the equivalence.

Procedure:　All the cards are shuffled and placed face down on the table. Each player takes a turn to turn over two cards. If the two totals, when the numbers or dots on the cards are added, are equivalent and the player claims them, he or she keeps them. If the cards are not equivalent they are replaced face down. The player with the most equivalent pairs of cards or dominoes at the end is the winner.

Stage 1 - dots only

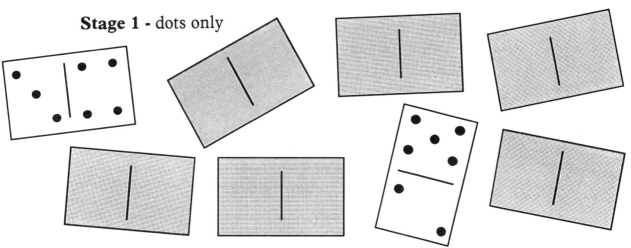

These two cards produce 3 + 4 and 5 + 2 so they are equivalent and "claimable".

Stage 2 - dots and numerals

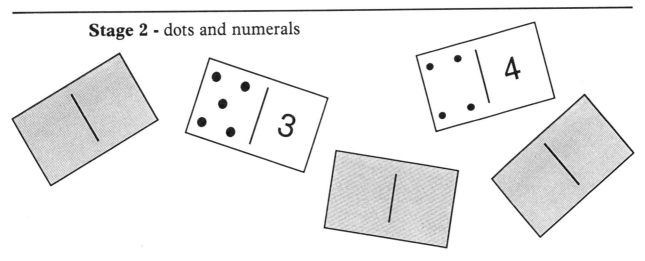

This pair is also "claimable" since 5 + 3 = 4 + 4.

Stage 3 - numbers only

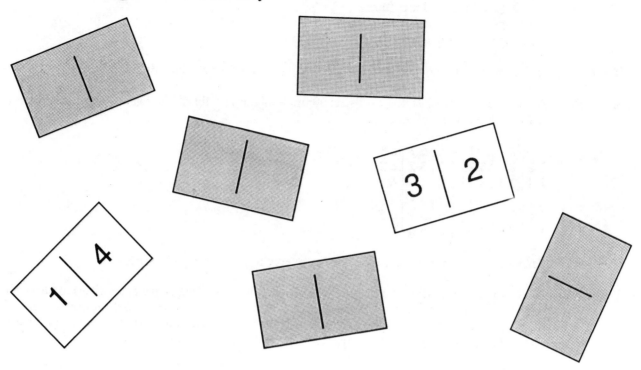

In this example 1 + 4 = 3 + 2 make an equivalent pair, so are 'claimable'.

Another easy version for children at the first stage is to use, instead of dominoes, the first ten cards of each suit of a pack of playing cards (hearts, spades, diamonds and clubs). Here the children play with 40 cards which will produce 20 pairs all told. The numbers can be whitened out.

A longer version for children at the second stage is to have the 40 playing cards (hearts, spades, diamonds and clubs) and four sets of cards (blank playing cards preferably with the same design on their backs as the playing cards) marked from 1 to 10. This gives 80 cards face down to start with which eventually produce 40 pairs. Again, the numerals on the playing cards can be covered with typewriting correction fluid.

Game 23   10's in a circle   Gamesheet 6

Objective: To practise the addition of two numbers to total 10.

Number of participants: Two.

Materials: An arrangement of numerals 1 to 9 round a circle as illustrated (drawn perhaps a little larger than here for young children); counters in two different colours for the two players.

Procedure: This is only part-competitive. Each child takes a turn at covering up two numbers that add up to 10. Extra motivation is sometimes provided if a stop watch is used to see if they can complete the circle quicker a second time.

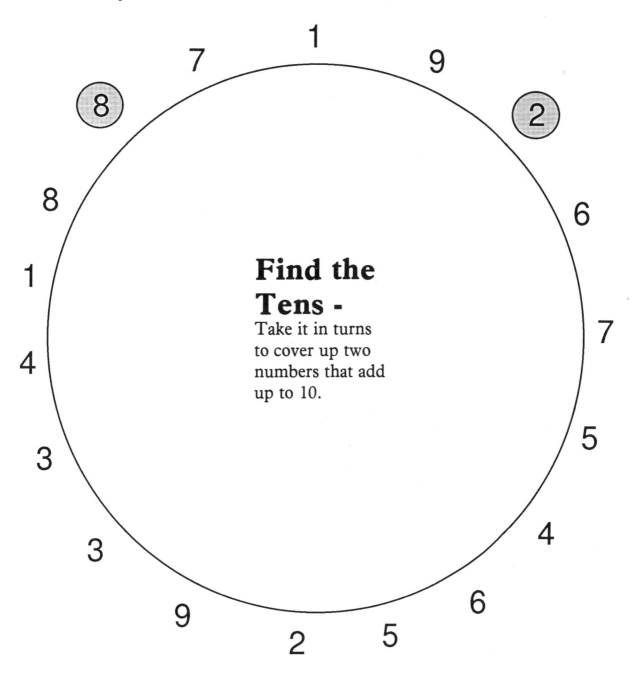

Find the Tens -
Take it in turns to cover up two numbers that add up to 10.

Game 24   Spin a number II

Objective: To practise addition bonds with totals from 2 to 9.

Number of participants: Two if each player takes 2 quarters of the board.
Four if each has one quarter.

Materials: A board and pointer as described for **Spin a number I**, Game 13 except that the numerals in each quarter are changed as indicated.

A set of 9 number-bond cards for each of the four players, coloured as indicated.

North (red) 1+1, 1+2, 3+2, 8+1, 1+8, 3+6, 6+1, 2+6, 3+5
East (blue) 1+5, 5+4, 7+2, 4+4, 3+4, 1+6, 2+4, 1+4, 2+1
South (yellow) 6+3, 4+5, 6+2, 7+1, 4+3, 4+2, 2+3, 3+1, 2+2
West (green) 2+7, 4+1, 1+3, 5+3, 1+7, 5+2, 2+5, 5+1, 3+3

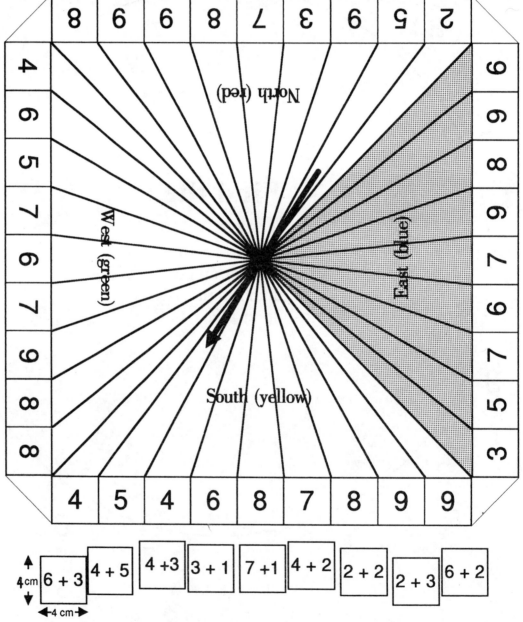

Procedure: Each player has his or her cards spread out near his/her quarter of the board (as South, above). The pointer is spun. When it comes to rest the player in whose quarter it points must place an appropriate card on the number indicated.
First to place all his/her tiles correctly wins.

Game 25   Shapes to 10

Objective: To practise addition of two or three numbers to totals up to 10.

Number of participants: One or several working individually.

Materials: Sheets with configurations such as those illustrated (drawn larger than here for young children); pencil and paper.

Procedure: 'Add up the numbers in each shape.'
(Introduce the vocabulary of shape: squares, triangle, etc.)

Example 1.

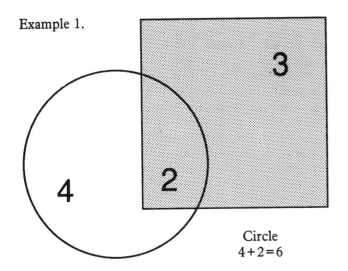

The shapes may be coloured or shaded to help younger children distinguish the shape and make the puzzle perceptually easier.

Circle   Square
4+2=6   2+3=5

Example 2.

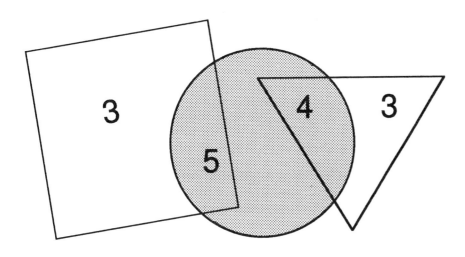

Square = 8   Circle = 9   Triangle = 7

Game 26   Straight lines for 10

Objective: To practise the addition of three numbers to total 10.

Number of participants: One (or several working separately)

Materials: A sheet (as illustrated); a ruler; a set of coloured pencils for each child.

Procedure: The child finds triples of numbers that make 10 when added, with the novelty that there is one number left over to find. Each 'triple' may be indicated by a different colour for ease of checking.

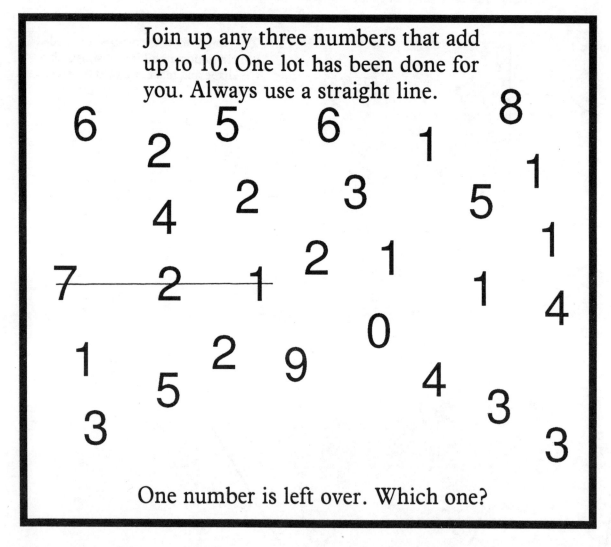

Join up any three numbers that add up to 10. One lot has been done for you. Always use a straight line.

6   5   6   8
   2   1
         2   3   1
      4   5
               2   1   1
7   2   1   1   4
                  0
   1   2   9   4
      5   3
   3   3

One number is left over. Which one?

Variations can be developed using almost any 'target' number and any quantity of numbers to add to the target amount.

Game 27   Missing numbers I

Objective: To develop and quicken recognition of number bonds from 5 to 9 using addition and subtraction.

Number of participants: One.

Materials: Use the grid below if 9 is the number to be practised; numeral cards 1 to 8 for 9 as the target; for a smaller target duplicate some of the numbered cards and outer numbers, a stop clock.

Procedure: The numeral cards are placed adjacent to the grid card and the child has to place the appropriate numeral card next to a grid number so that they make the total in the centre.

After a trial run, the child can time him or herself over, say, three tries.
If appropriate to your children you can arrange races as an extra motivator.

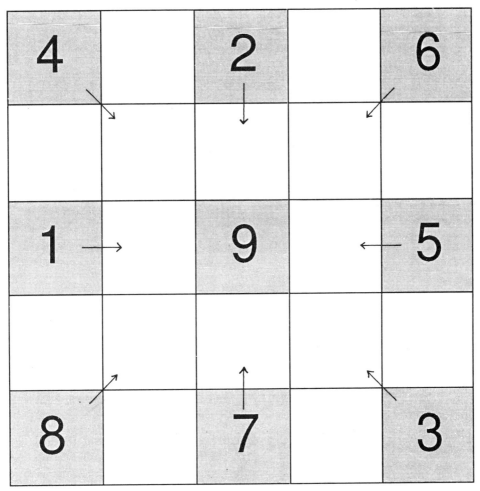

Paste number 1 to 8 on to card and cut out.

1	2	3	4

5	6	7	8

Game 28   Patterns with 10

Objective: To reinforce addition facts to 10 in the context of developing visual patterns.

Number of participants: Individuals.

Materials: Prepared sheets as illustrated; coloured crayons; rulers; (wood sheets; nails; hammer; coloured thread if '3D' decorative versions are desired).

Procedure: 'Use your rulers and coloured pencils to join the numbers that add up to 10. The first line has been done for you each time.'

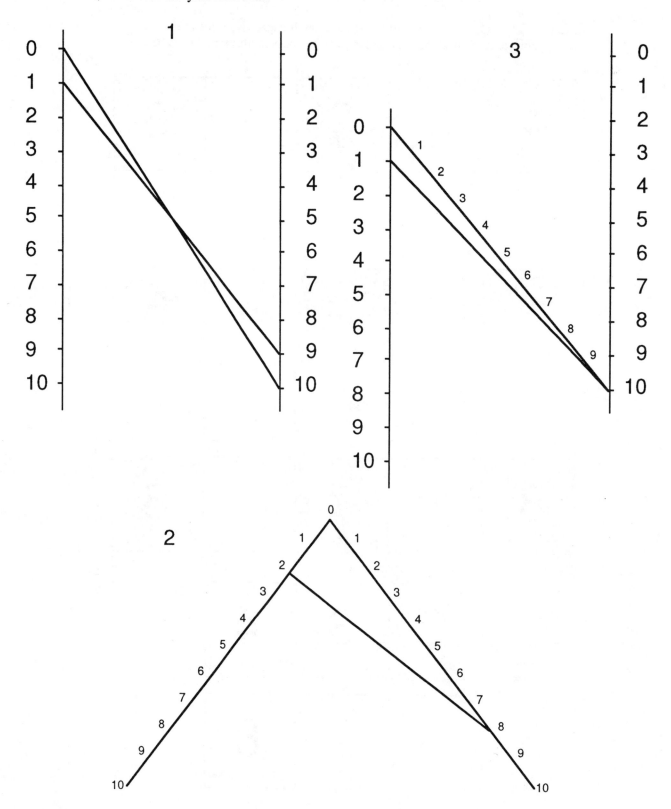

Game 29   Frame the tens

Objective: To practise addition of four numbers to total 10.

Number of participants: One, or a group working as individuals.

Materials: Grids as illustrated, coloured pencils, a ruler, and 'window' cards (for 4 squares).

Procedure: Read the rubric in each frame with the player. Explain how to crayon round the squares when identified.

The four numbers in the 'window' add up to 10.

Move the window card and find some more lots of four numbers that make 10.

There are three more lots of four, little squares that will make a big square of 10.

Use a coloured pencil and draw a square round each lot of four numbers that make 10.

Write the four numbers in each big square in your book, like this:

3 + 5 + 1 + 1 = 10

2	4	1	3	4
3	5	2	2	1
1	1	3	5	3
3	2	5	2	5
4	1	5	2	1

The four numbers in the black square add up to 10.

Find some more lots of four numbers that make 10.

You can use a little square more than once.

There are six more lots of 10 in big squares. Try to find them all.

Colour each big square in a different colour.

2	4	0	3	4
3	5	1	2	1
1	1	2	5	2
3	2	4	2	6
3	2	5	2	0

Note: The lower frame includes the numeral '0'. Also some of the squares overlap which some children may find perceptually confusing.

Game 30   Wheelies I

Objective: To practise subtraction from numbers from 4 to 9.

Number of participants: One.

Materials: Concentric cardboard circles fastened together with a paper fastener so that they rotate; pencil and paper if required.

Procedure: Ask the child to solve the subtraction problems (as illustrated for a novice), then rotate the wheel(s) to produce a new set of problems. A timing element may be introduced if you think it suitable for the child using this apparatus.

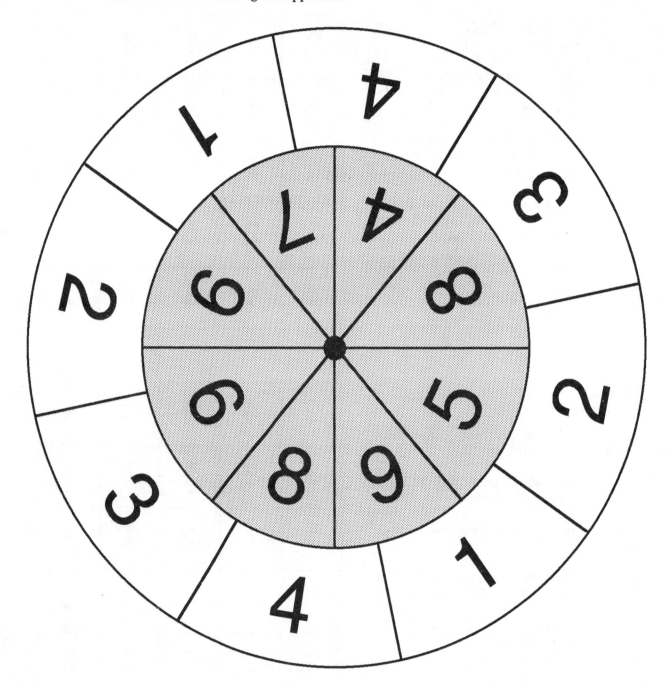

Note: This format will produce a total of 25 different problems, 7 of them occuring more than once.

This versatile apparatus, using different numerals can be adapted for almost any problem involving the four basic processes. After the introduction of place-value, the numerals included above can be used for addition up to totals of 13.

Game 31   Magic Triangles I

Objective: A more difficult game to practise number combinations to 9, 10 and 11. Useful prior to introduction of place-value.

Number of participants: Individuals or pairs.

Materials: Equilateral triangle as illustrated. Six number cards 1 - 6.

Procedure: Pupils are asked to put the number cards on the triangle so that each side adds up to 9. To give initial help, put the 2 on the apex and the 5 in the middle of the base. Subsequently, use the same cards to make totals of 10 and 11.

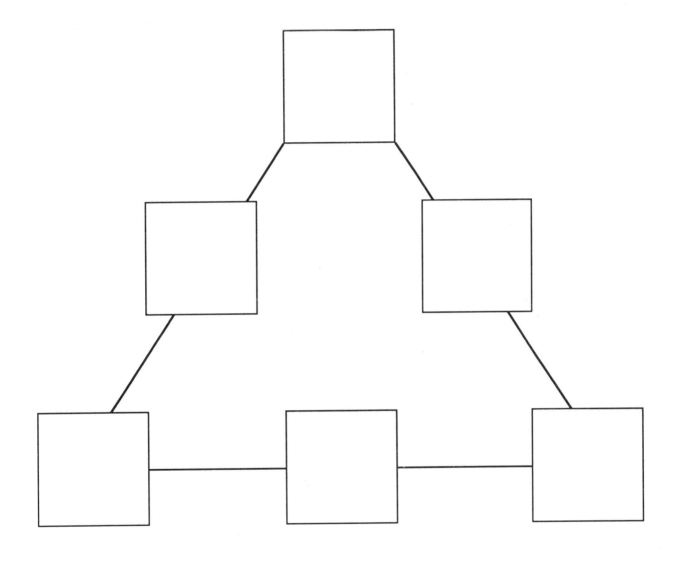

Game 32　　　The race card

Objective:　　To practise addition bonds to 10, introducing a speed element.
　　　　　　　(A useful activity immediately prior to the introduction of place-value).

Number of participants: One or several children of matched ability.

Materials:　　Pads of 'race' slips as illustrated; pencils; a timer.

⑩ a	⑩ b	⑩ c	⑩ d	⑩ e
2 + ☐	3 + ☐	5 + ☐	5 + ☐	8 + ☐
3 + ☐	4 + ☐	4 + ☐	7 + ☐	7 + ☐
1 + ☐	1 + ☐	3 + ☐	3 + ☐	9 + ☐
4 + ☐	6 + ☐	2 + ☐	6 + ☐	6 + ☐
6 + ☐	2 + ☐	7 + ☐	8 + ☐	5 + ☐
5 + ☐	5 + ☐	1 + ☐	1 + ☐	4 + ☐
8 + ☐	9 + ☐	9 + ☐	9 + ☐	2 + ☐
7 + ☐	7 + ☐	8 + ☐	3 + ☐	3 + ☐
9 + ☐	8 + ☐	6 + ☐	4 + ☐	1 + ☐

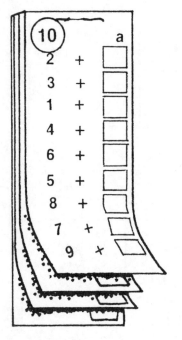

Procedure:　　Prepare sheets of problems, cut into strips (as pictured) and staple the strips as on the left. The problems are graded approximately for difficulty from trial and error with groups of children.

Say 'See how quickly you can write in the missing numbers to make ten every time'.

As the children complete their one strip they fold them over and press on with the next page. If one child is working alone, he or she tries the pad again trying to beat his/her first time for completion. With a group, the fastest one with correct answers wins.

Game 33   Spiral Ludo

Objective: To provide practice in counting on and counting back.

Number of participants: Two.

Materials: Two counters for each player; a die inscribed with +2, +4 and +6, −1, −2 and −3; a spiral number track.

Procedure: 'You each have two soldiers in prison and you want them to escape. They have to go down the spiral track to freedom. Sometimes they have to dodge back and keep out of sight of the guards.

Roll the die. If it's a plus number you can go forward. If it's a minus number you must go back. The first player to get both soldiers through the gate at the end of the track is the winner.'

Roll the die for starter. The higher positive number starts.
At the finish (gate) the exact number must be obtained to get through.

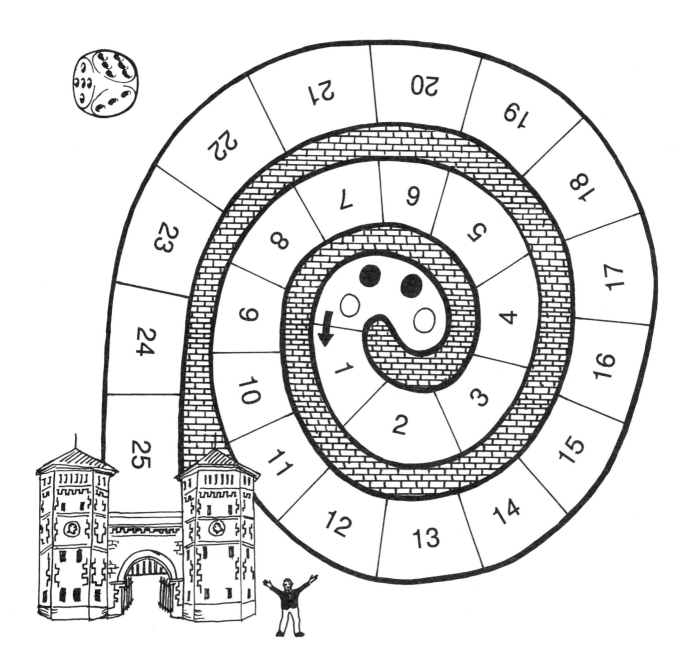

Game 34   Spiral numbers

Objective: To provide practice in counting up to 6 places forward and 2 places backward.

Number of participants: Two.

Materials: A number line as illustrated, the actual size appropriate to the dexterity of the children playing the game; counters; a die and shaker.

Procedure: The two competitors throw for first go: higher score goes first. Each throws the die and moves the counter along the track the number of spaces shown on the die. When it lands on a 'squared' number, a predetermined bonus amount is added. If this is 2 and a 6 has been thrown the counter is moved a total of 8 places. If the counter lands on a 'circled' space the predetermined amount from the thrown score is subtracted; so if a 6 is thrown, the player would end up only 4 spaces further on. Note: if a player lands on another space that is 'squared' or 'circled' after adjusting his/her 'thrown' score, he/she ignores this add on or subtract instruction.

| 1 | 2 | 3 | 4 | 5 | (6) | [7] | 8 |

9

| [21] | 22 | 23 | (24) | ✳25✳ | | | (10) |

| (20) | | | | | | | [11] |

| 19 | 18 | 17 | [16] | (15) | 14 | 13 | 12 |

◯ GO BACK 2   ☐ GO ON 2

Game 35 In the lift

Objective: To provide practice in counting up to 6 places, forwards and backwards, within the range 1 to 21.

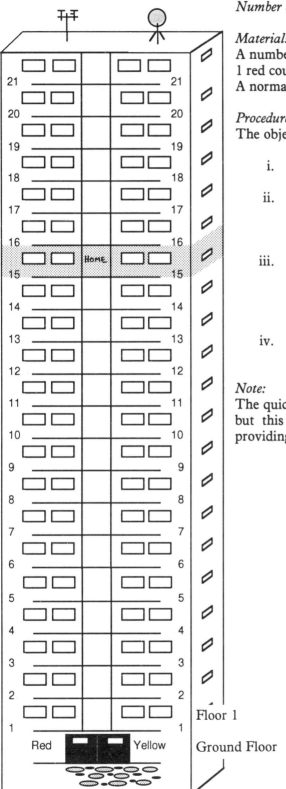

Number of participants: Two.

Materials:
A number line (as diagram) presented as a block of flats.
1 red counter; 1 yellow counter.
A normal die; marked 1 — 6.

Procedure:
The objective is to land the counter exactly on floor 15.

i. Each pupil has one throw of die; the highest number starts.

ii. Starting at the ground floor, the pupils throw the die alternately, moving up the number of floors indicated on the die.

iii. If the number thrown takes the counter beyond the 15th floor, the counter remains on the higher floor. The next turn the counter will be moved *down* according to the number thrown.

iv. Continue moving up and down until the counter lands exactly on the 15th floor.

Note:
The quickest any pupil can reach the 15th floor is after 3 throws — but this is unlikely. However the movement up and down is providing enjoyable addition and subtraction practice.

Game 36   Number series II

Objective: Ordering randomly presented numerals up to 100.

Number of participants: One, or pairs working in consultation.

Materials: Framed sets of numbers as illustrated.

Procedure: Players follow instructions given in frames (see NUMBER SERIES I, Game 19).

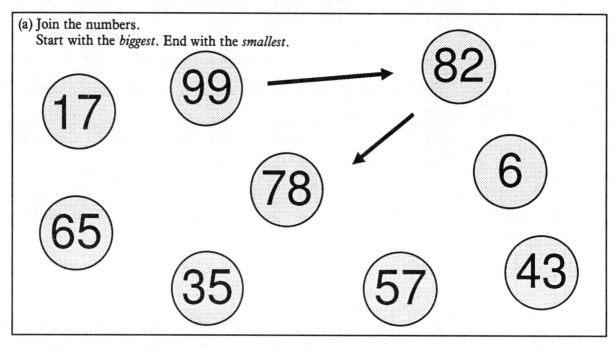

(a) Join the numbers.
    Start with the *biggest*. End with the *smallest*.

This example helps to practise discrimination between numbers with transposed digits: e.g. 64 and 46.

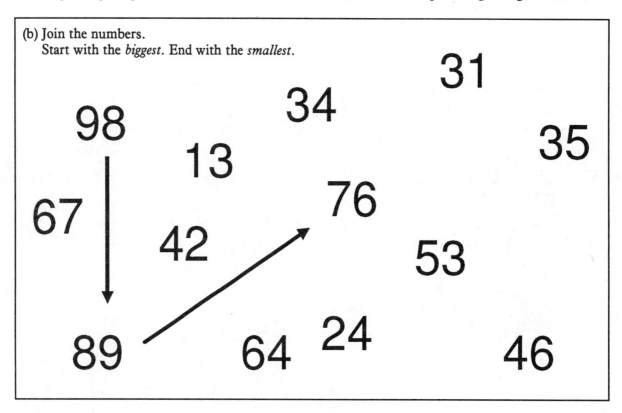

(b) Join the numbers.
    Start with the *biggest*. End with the *smallest*.

In each of these the order of working can (and should) be reversed from time to time: i.e. one time start with the biggest number; when mastery of this is apparent, start with the smallest and vice versa.

Game 37   Number chains

Objective: To practise the determination of numbers at fixed intervals (number chains) involving addition and subtraction to 55.

Number chains or patterns can be plotted on number (100) squares and on number lines as well as on displays as shown here; indeed they should, because the concepts are thereby presented in several different ways.

Number of participants: One, or pairs working in consultation.

Materials: Prepared sheets of numbers as illustrated here (use A4 size at least for young children); pencils.

Procedure: (a) Present a completed sheet so that the child(ren) has to *recognise* the chain/pattern. (This is an easier task than *establishing* a chain). 'Can you find the pattern in these numbers? What happens when the arrow moves on each time?' 'The first number is increased by two. Then it happens again, and again.' In this example, the numbers are also all odd ones and the child might recognise this fact.

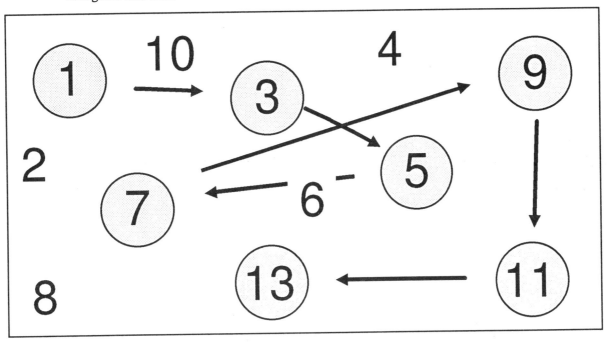

(b) Here the child has to find the pattern from the given start. "The pattern has been started. Can you finish it?"

In both (a) and (b) the pupil has to ignore the 'diversionary' numbers: evens in (a), odds in (b).

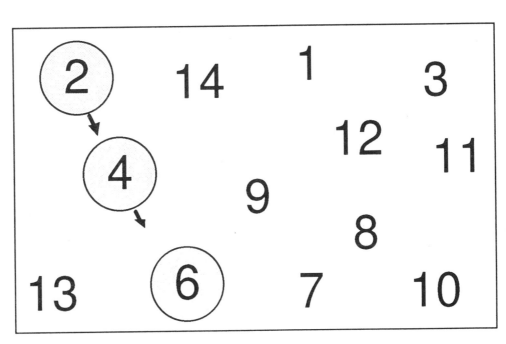

49

Three more examples of chains/patterns that can be used both for recognition and discovery of number patterns.

(c) The +3 chain.

In each of these there are no diversionary numbers to contend with.

Always ask the child(ren) to give the rule for the chain.

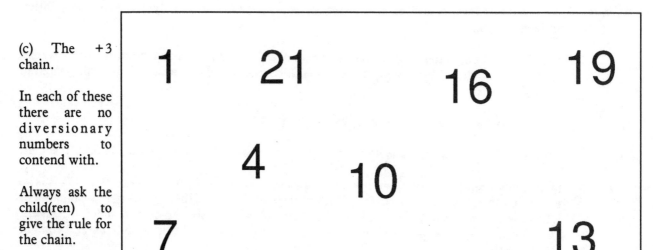

(d) The -3 chain.

14   2   26   32

23   11   8   17

5   20   29

(e) The 'add-an-extra-1-each-time' chain (triangular numbers).

6   28   45   10

55   3

21   15   36

Most children will be content with 'It's getting bigger each time' as an explanation. Draw the triangles with the child to elicit a more precise description of the number pattern. Seek everyday examples of triangular numbers, e.g. stacked tins of food.

Game 38　　Got It! II　　Gamesheet 9

Objective:　To identify a chosen number between 1 and 100 by questioning.

Number of participants: Three, four or five.

Materials:　Number square(s), pencil(s).

Procedure:　One child acts as quiz master/mistress and chooses a number between 1 and 100. She or he keeps the number to herself. The others have to discover or guess the number by asking questions. The quiz person may only answer 'Yes' or 'No'. The object is to discover the number in as few questions as possible.

The game can be the panel against the quiz person and, rather like Twenty Questions, if they guess the number in ten questions or fewer they gain a point; if it takes more than ten, the quiz person has one. The best of five is about the right length of time for this activity.

The children take turns to ask the questions. At first they will tend to ask random questions or to guess the number. Occasionally, they will be successful, but usually not by this haphazard method and gradually they will ask 'strategic' questions especially if they use the 100 number square to keep a record of which numbers they have eliminated.

'Is it more than 10?' 'Yes.'
'Is it more than 20?' 'Yes.'
'Is it less than 90?' 'No.' etc.

Game 39   Chance   Gamesheet 10

Objective: Adding or subtracting to plus or minus 3, starting with 10 coins.

Number of participants: Two.

Materials: Board as illustrated, 24cm × 15cm or larger, drawn in forty 3cm squares; 40 plastic 2p pieces or counters; one die faced: +1, +2, +3, −1, −2 and −3.

Procedure: Each player starts with 10 coins on the board. They take it in turns to throw the die. If a plus number is obtained they take further coins (1, 2 or 3) from the common 'purse' and place them in squares on their side of the board. If a minus number is shown that many coins are removed from the original ten on their side of the board. The game proceeds until one of the players fills all his or her 20 squares or, alternatively, until a player loses all his ten coins.

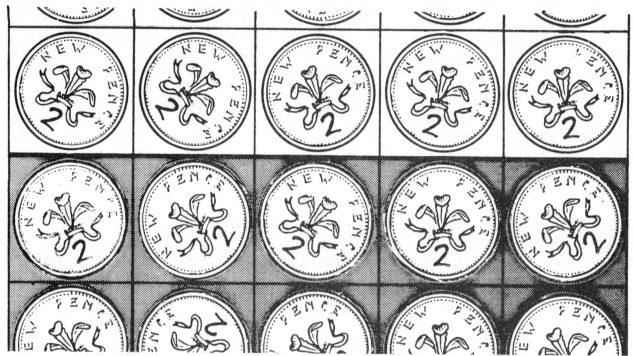

Variation 1:   The game can involve larger numbers by using a larger board (e.g. 10 by 10 squares) and the players starting with 50 plastic coins in place. Two dice are used, the numbers obtained summed e.g. $-3+2=1$ or multiplied e.g. $(-3) \times (+3) = -9$.

Variation 2:   A larger board, and two dice with faces +1, +1, +2, +2, +3 and +3 used. The players roll the dice alternately as usual, but the sum of each player's first roll is added to his board total so he or she places more coins on the board, and the second of his/her throws is subtracted so coins are removed. For a shorter game use the original board as drawn on this page.

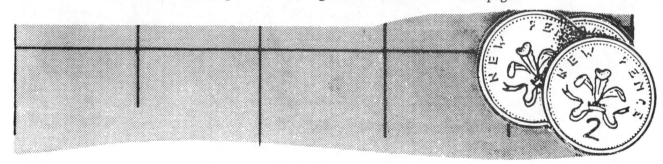

Game 40   Pay up   Gamesheet 11

Objective: To consolidate the concept of equivalence of coinage; totalling coins to 65 pence.

Number of participants: Two up to four and a "banker."

Materials: A quantity of plastic (or real) coins of various denominations, a counter for each player, a die marked 1 to 6. Board marked as below.

Procedure: Each player has £1 in mixed plastic coins from the "bank." They take turns to throw the die and move their counter on the indicated number of spaces. The youngest player starts, or the one with the biggest feet, or whatever.

           If the player lands on a white space she hands the amount shown to the bank; if she lands on a coloured space she takes that amount from the bank. The one with the most money at the end is the winner. The player or banker claims the amount according to the square with the call 'Pay up!'.

           These are minimum sizes. Remember each space may need to accommodate more than one counter.

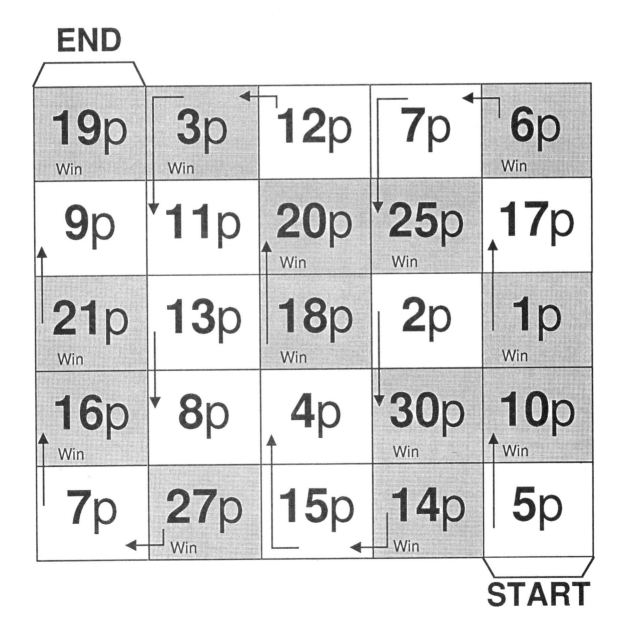

Game 41   Making money

Objective: To practise totalling coins to 25 pence, using a stipulated number of coins. The variation (page 55) requires similar skills but calls for more sophisticated strategies.

Number of participants: Two.

Materials: A list of amounts of money (such as illustrated), counters, a die marked 1 to 6, plastic coins, pencil and paper.

Procedure: The players take turns to roll the die. According to the number shown they may take that number of coins from the bank to make the amount shown on the list.

If the player can take the number of coins shown and make the amount on the list he/she keeps them, and places one of his or her counters on the amount to show it has been used. (If the money list has been duplicated then the player can write his or her name on the amount instead.)

The second player then has a turn, rolls the die and hopes to find suitable coins.

When all the squares are taken the players add up the cash they have won. The highest total wins.

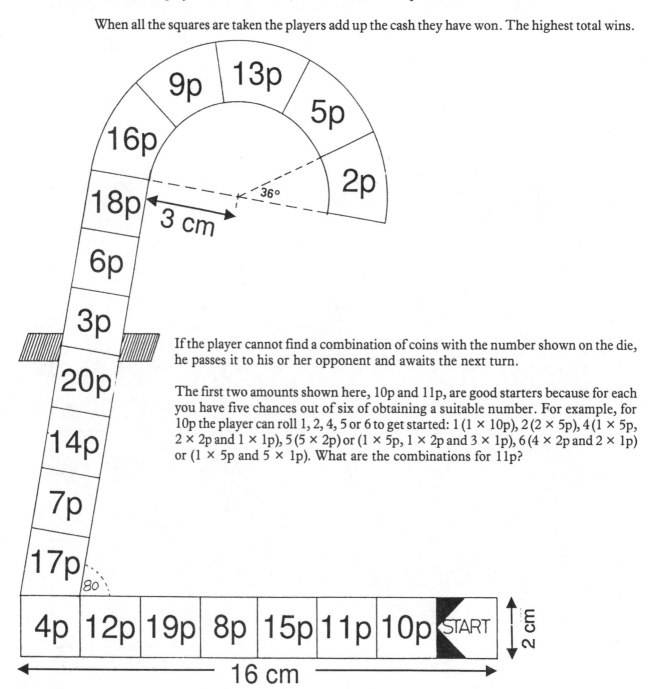

If the player cannot find a combination of coins with the number shown on the die, he passes it to his or her opponent and awaits the next turn.

The first two amounts shown here, 10p and 11p, are good starters because for each you have five chances out of six of obtaining a suitable number. For example, for 10p the player can roll 1, 2, 4, 5 or 6 to get started: 1 (1 × 10p), 2 (2 × 5p), 4 (1 × 5p, 2 × 2p and 1 × 1p), 5 (5 × 2p) or (1 × 5p, 1 × 2p and 3 × 1p), 6 (4 × 2p and 2 × 1p) or (1 × 5p and 5 × 1p). What are the combinations for 11p?

This track allows for inflation! For this one £3 for each player is about right. Note you must make sure no one goes bankrupt. Do this by making most spaces gains and with most of these among the higher amounts of money in the game.

It is also best to have mostly gains near the end of the track so that the unfortunates who have lost a lot will make up their losses — and cheer up!

If the teacher can keep watch on the game, it is sometimes useful for the children to have pencil and paper and keep running totals with each throw. This gives plenty of practice and provides something to do between turns.

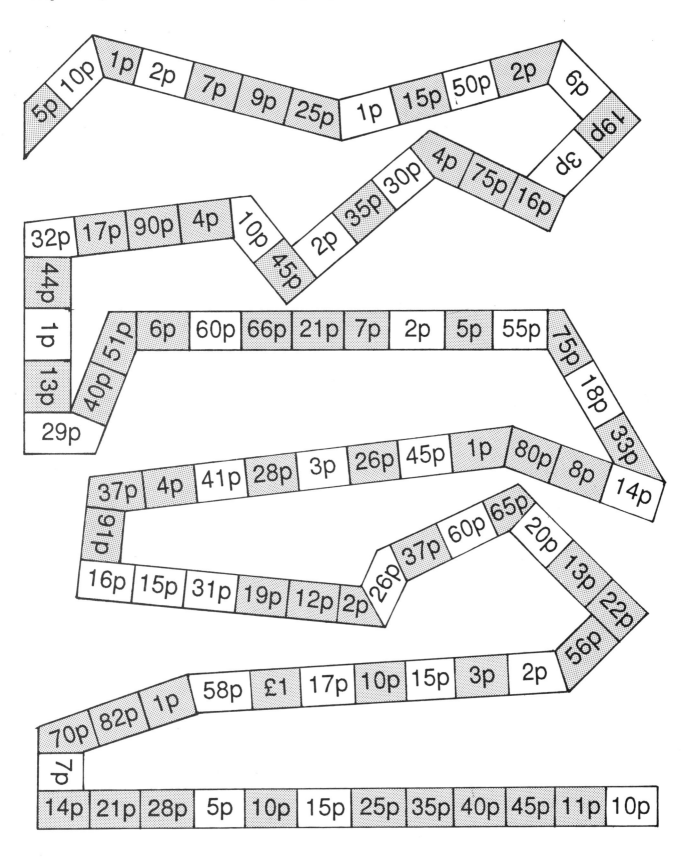

Variation: Here the two players take turns to roll the die, as before, and, having obtained a number (1 to 6) the player then examines the vacant amount squares and nominates the one he or she is going to 'claim.' The amount squares may be 'claimed' in any order unlike the first version.

The aim of this game is as previously, by the end to accumulate a higher total than your opponent and with an open choice of amount squares, tactics can be employed. For example, the player may obtain 3 on the die. On the board both 9p and 22p are available. The wise player will choose the 22p square (2 × 10p and 1 × 2p) rather than the 9p one (1 × 5p and 2 × 2p). The players are encouraged to go for the larger amounts even if it means more thinking and calculation.

As with all games, when the chance element is reduced as here, it is prudent to match the two protagonists as evenly as possible.

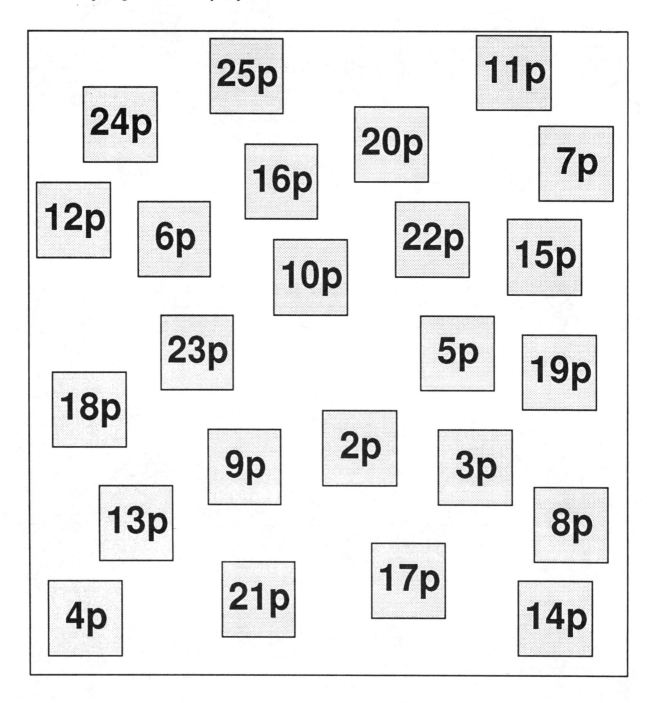

Level 3

Refer to notes on place-value (pp 125-6) prior to the use of games at Level 3.

Reading, writing and ordering number to 1000.

Learning and using addition and subtraction facts to 20 (including zero).
As preparation for Level 4, Games 59 and 60 introduce totals between 20 and 40.

Learning and using multiplication facts up to 5 × 5.

Games to develop calculator keying skills.
One hundred percent accuracy in keying skills is a pre-requisite to the meaningful and confident use of the calculator. Games designed solely to assist in the development of accurate keying skills may draw upon a mathematical content beyond the immediate understanding of the pupil. However, at this stage the priority lies in the satisfaction of achieving the correct response to the keying involved. Possible insights into future potentialities of the calculator could be a bonus!

Calculator games marked

Game 42   Making numbers

Objective: Making two and three-figure numbers from given cards and comparing values of those numbers.

Number of participants: One or a group.

Materials: Card numerals; pencils; paper.

Procedure: 'You have five cards: 0, 1, 2, 3 and 4. See how many different numbers you can make when you use two at a time.'
Demonstrate: '1 and 0 can stand for 10. 2 and 1 can stand for 21, or (transpose the cards) 12.'

(a) Have the children write down each number as they show it with the digits saying how many tens and ones each digit represents.

The numbers available from these five cards are:
10, 20, 30, 40;
12, 13, 14;
21, 23, 24;
31, 32, 34;
41, 42, 43;
'Which is the biggest? ... the smallest?'

0	1	2	3	4

(b) 'This time take any three of the cards. How many different numbers can you make?'

Demonstrate with, say, 1, 3 and 4. 'With these you can make 134 (one hundred and thirty four), or 143 (say each number as you move the cards and make a new number), or 314 ..., 341 ..., 431 ..., 413 ...'

1	3	4
1	4	3

etc.

58

(c) Take three cards and ask the child(ren) to list the numbers made from the three digits between two limits: e.g.

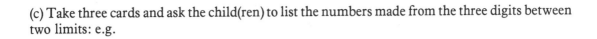

'Write down all the numbers made from these three cards less than 300, but greater than 123.'

The children then experiment and shuffle the cards to produce the following. They record these on paper or in their books.

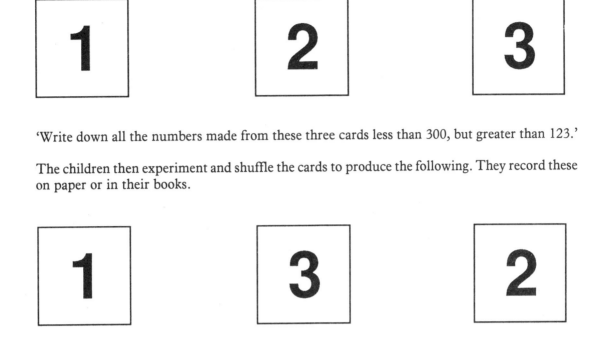

The children might go on to demonstrate that these numbers are within the prescribed limits by working out how much bigger than 123 each of their numbers is, and how much smaller than 300. But this will depend on your group's ability.

(d) In each of these activities the difficulty is, of course, increased with the number of numeral cards used. The task is also made longer, so beware of boredom if the children have to labour at it.

Game 43   Gamble

Objective: Sequencing and comparing the value of three-figure numbers.

Number of participants: Groups, no particular number.

Materials: Numeral cards marked 0 to 9 (10 in all); squared paper at least three columns wide; pencils.

Procedure: The object is to write down the largest number possible using three numerals displayed randomly. The numeral cards are shuffled. One is drawn from the pack at random. The children write that number in a square of their choosing.

Child A    Child B 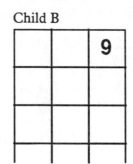   Child C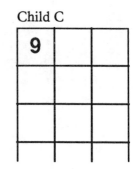

Here the first number drawn was 9. Child A has chosen to place it in column 2, child B in column 3 and child C in column 1.

A second card is drawn and shown. Again the children write it in either of the vacant squares along the top row.

Child A   Child B 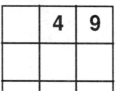   Child C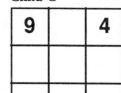

A third number card is drawn and displayed and the children write it in the vacant square. The child with the biggest number and who can read it wins a point. So in this round the winner would be child C.

Child A   Child B   Child C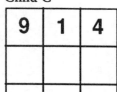

Note: The number must be written in as soon as it is shown. The players must commit themselves immediately. Have ten rounds in any one game. The larger the group of children, the more will get the largest possible number each time, but the number of columns can be increased gradually until all the ten number cards are needed. Then there will probably be an outright individual winner.

Variations: (1) Let the smallest number be the winner each time.

(2) Let the winner be the largest odd number, smallest odd number, or perhaps the largest or smallest even number each time.

(3) The winner could be the player with the largest/smallest number divisible by 3, 4 or 5 — or any divisor for that matter.

Game 44   Got it! III   Gamesheet 12

Objective: To identify an unknown number under 1000 by questioning, building the number from given components.

(See notes on questioning strategies in **Got It I**, Game 21, and **Got It II**, Game 38).

Number of participants: One working with the teacher, or a two-team game.

Materials: Number cards as illustrated; chalkboard and chalk.

Procedure: Place the number cards face up on the table, and the teacher secretly chooses a number, say 346, between 312 and 546.

0 ones	**1 one**	**2 ones**	**3 ones**	**4 ones**
5 ones	**10 ones**	**11 ones**	**12 ones**	
3 tens	**4 tens**	**5 tens**	**40 tens**	**41 tens**
42 tens	**43 tens**	**45 tens**	**51 tens**	
3 hundreds	**5 hundreds**			

The teacher says 'I have this number (for example) 312.' It is written up and said. 'And that one, 546' which is also written up and said. 'I am thinking of a number which comes in between those two. Find the number by guessing.' In answer to guesses the teacher says only 'bigger' or 'smaller' until the child or team guess the correct one. (The opposing team leader can take the place of the teacher.) When the number is guessed, the child or team must construct the number (its equivalence) using the cards. One point is awarded for each correct construction; another may be awarded for each correct guess in under twenty tries (like *Twenty Questions*). Members of each team take alternate turns.

The team/child with the most points wins.

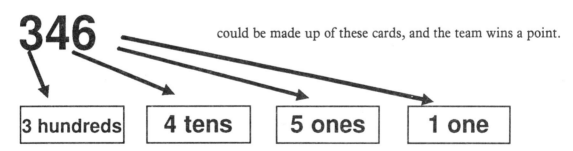

346 could be made up of these cards, and the team wins a point.

61

Game 45 Dice Games

Objective: To practise addition to 12 (or subtraction from 6) using two dice, including a speed element.

Number of participants: A group as large as about ten or fewer, as individuals or in teams.

Materials: Two dice with numbers or dots or mixed to give a variety of presentation; a bell or buzzer or audible timer of some kind.

Procedure: Roll the two dice. The children in turn must quickly add the two uppermost numbers. Each correct answer is rewarded with a counter or tally. Use a timer to indicate a time limit if you wish to make the game more frantic! (One for the ends of lessons perhaps!)

More spots for subtraction or counting on.

Participants and materials: As above.

Procedure: Roll two dice. 'How many more spots/more on one than on the other?' (Differently coloured dice can help to make this instruction more explicit.) Be prepared: 'Are they the same?' The timer can be used as in the first game if desired.
Stick on labels with larger numbers than conventional dice present for older/more able pupils.

Rolling for simple addition and probability.

Number of participants: Individuals or pairs.

Materials: Two dice; number graph (see below); a pencil.

Procedure: The 'investigators' roll the dice many times (one hundred is suggested) and they record the sum of the two numbers that appear. This sum is anything from 2 to 12 with orthodox dice.

2	3	4	5	6	7	8	9	10	11	12
✓		✓	✓	✓	✓	✓	✓		✓	
			✓	✓	✓	✓	✓			
				✓	✓					
					✓					
					etc.					

Discuss the results.
Yes, even the
bottom set at maths
can do this!

Game 46   Number bond race

Objective: Practice in the addition of two numbers, each between 0 and 9, including a speed element.

Number of participants: Two.

Materials: Two playing boards each 60cm × 40cm and each divided into 100 rectangles (6cm × 4cm), as illustrated; each board requires 100 'answer' cards (5cm × 3cm); a timer (a stop clock or a watch with a second hand).

0 + 0	0 + 1	0 + 2	0 + 3	0 + 4	0 + 5	0 + 6	0 + 7	0 + 8	0 + 9
1 + 0	1 + 1	1 + 2	1 + 3	1 + 4	1 + 5	1 + 6	**8**	1 + 8	1 + 9
2 + 0	2 + 1	**4**	2 + 3	2 + 4	2 + 5	2 + 6	2 + 7	2 + 8	**11**
3 + 0	3 + 1	3 + 2	3 + 3	3 + 4	3 + 5	3 + 6	3 + 7	**11**	3 + 9
4 + 0	4 + 1	4 + 2	4 + 3	4 + 4	4 + 5	4 + 6	**11**	4 + 8	4 + 9
5 + 0	**6**	5 + 2	5 + 3	5 + 4	5 + 5	5 + 6	5 + 7	5 + 8	5 + 9
6 + 0	6 + 1	6 + 2	6 + 3	6 + 4					
7	7 + 1	7 + 2	**10**	7 + 4					
8 + 0	8 + 1	8 + 2	8 + 3	8 + 4					
9 + 0	9 + 1	9 + 2	9 + 3	9 + 4	9 + 5	9 + 6	9 + 7	9 + 8	9 + 9

40 cm

60 cm

It is convenient to use two different colours for the 'answer' cards. Those that have to be placed to the left of the thick line might be yellow, those to the right orange. If you haven't card of different colours, use different coloured inks.

3 cm

5 cm

Procedure: (a) Two players:
Each player has a board and a set of 'answer' cards. The answer cards are shuffled and stacked face up. On the word 'Go' the competitors take one 'answer' card at a time and place it on the appropriate 'bond' rectangle. The first one to place all his or her 'answers' correctly wins.

The game is made easier when only two are playing by using only the left side of the board and its 'answers'. It would help the child if the unused half were to be folded under or covered.

Extension: May also be adapted for −, × and ÷ games, with an appropriate change of title.

Game 47   Shapes to twenty

Objective: To practice addition of up to four numbers with totals up to 20. (See **Shapes to ten**, Game 25).

Number of participants: Individual working.

Materials: Sheets with configurations such as that illustrated. Pencil and paper.

Procedure: "Add the numbers in each shape." Use the opportunity for ensuring that the pupils can name the shapes.

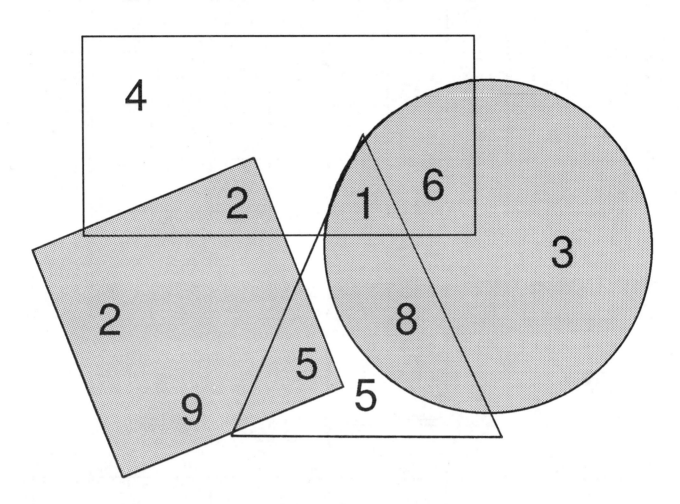

Game 48   Magic Square

Objective: To arrange the numbers 1 to 9 in a magic square so that the horizontal and vertical columns, and the diagonals, each total 15.

Number of participants: Individual children.

Materials: The 3 × 3 square as illustrated in **Fifteens**, Game 58.
Cards from 1 to 9 to fit the smaller squares.

Procedure: Explain the objective as given above. Use this opportunity, as appropriate, to consolidate the mathematical terms in the objectives.

Game 49　Make 11 (or 12 or 13 etc)　

Objective:　To practise addition of numbers with totals from 10 to 20.

Number of participants: Two.

Materials:　A separate card for each number from 10 to 20 (as illustrated). A supply of counters for each player, of sufficient size to cover the numbers — a different colour for each player.

Procedure:　(a) Roll a die to decide who starts the first game, then for further games start alternately. The players take it in turns to cover a number adding this number to a running total as each is covered. The player whose counter makes the total exactly 11 (or 13 or 15 etc) wins.

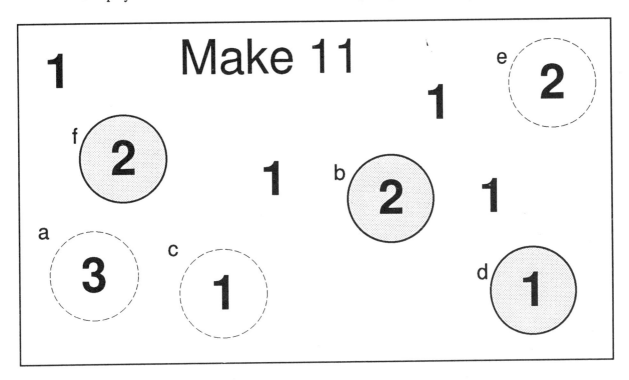

For example, in the illustration above, the sequence of this game was:
(a) 3 (3 running total) — (b) 2 (5 running total) — (c) 1 (6 running total) — (d) 1 (7 running total) — (e) 2 (9 running total) — (f) 2 (11 running total)
so the player whose counters are shaded in the picture won.

Gradually increase the target figure (and provide new playing cards with more and higher numerals).

At any stage the two opponents can play a set of five games at a time.

A class knockout competition can be organised.

(b) Subtraction: Make 0. Start with a number say 21, and subtract each number covered by a counter. The player to reach exactly 0 wins.

Note:　More numbers than those on the card illustrated are needed for this. (2 more given on Gamesheet).

Game 50   Legs eleven!

Objective: To identify four numbers that can be added or subtracted to give an answer of 11. Later variations can introduce × and ÷.

Number of participants: Four.

Materials: Four sets of number cards labelled 1 to 10, 40 in all. Normal playing cards are suitable.

Procedure: The 40 cards are well shuffled and dealt into four sets face down. Each of the four players holds his/her cards face down and in turn places one face up. If preferred, the cards can be placed side by side in the middle of the table.

Whenever any combination of the cards on view make 11, the player spotting this first and calling 'legs!' takes all the cards covered by those that make 11.

For example:

Here 3 + 7 + 1 = 11, so the player noticing this combination can claim the three piles beneath these numbers.

The order of play should be kept to throughout with any winner turning over the first card after a successful claim.

Decide before the game begins whether or not players who have no cards left automatically drop out or still observe and shout 'Legs!' at an appropriate moment.

Variations: Some examples for the more sophisticated!

These can produce: 3 × 2 + 4 + 1 = 11.

These 9 + 9 + 4 ÷ 2 = 11. So a claim for all four piles each time is possible.

66

Game 51 Addition squares

Objective: To practise the addition of two numbers; each from 0 to 10.

Number of participants: Individuals or a group/class.

Materials: Each child requires a sheet of squared paper (12 × 12) the measure depending on the maturity and motor control of individual pupils. The drawing here is suitable for many young and middle juniors.

	0	1	2	3	4	5	6	7	8	9	10
10											
9											
8											
7											
6							12				
5						10					
4					8						
3		4		6							
2	2	3	4								
1	1	2	3								
0	0	1									
+	0	1	2	3	4	5	6	7	8	9	10

Procedure: Each child completes the square using the columns (as in 'He read the column in the paper') and rows (as in 'a row of chairs'). Can the children spot interesting patterns, e.g. the doubles?

Notes: Practical — for those with visuo-motor co-ordination difficulties or visual perception problems a L-shaped or (better) a mask with an inverted L-shape cut-out obscures intrusive other numbers and keeps the correct target numbers in view.

10										20
9									18	
8								16		
7							14			
6						12				
5					10					

	3				6			18				
								6		8	9	10

The 'doubles' diagonal

Any other patterns?

Extension: The commutative law for addition may be introduced or reinforced using the addition square.

The commutative law: the order you add the numbers does not matter. The total is always the same (e.g. 3 + 2 = 5, 2 + 3 = 5).

If the addition square is drawn on tracing paper by folding the square along the south west — north east diagonal (the diagonal with 0, 2, 4, 6, 8 etc on it) each answer will be seen back to back with its twin: for example, 10 (9 + 1) will back on 10 (1 + 9).

The children can then record this as
    9 + 1 = 10
    1 + 9 = 10
    so
    9 + 1 = 10 = 1 + 9
    or
    10 = 9 + 1 = 1 + 9 etc.

Game 52   Choose your number

Objectives: To practise addition to 18 using two numbers. To practise subtraction from numbers less than 10.

Number of participants: Two.

Materials: Two sets of cards (8cm × 5cm) on which the numerals 1 to 9 (for addition) are written, and two further cards for 0 (for the subtraction game). Twenty cards are required altogether, for both addition and subtraction activities.

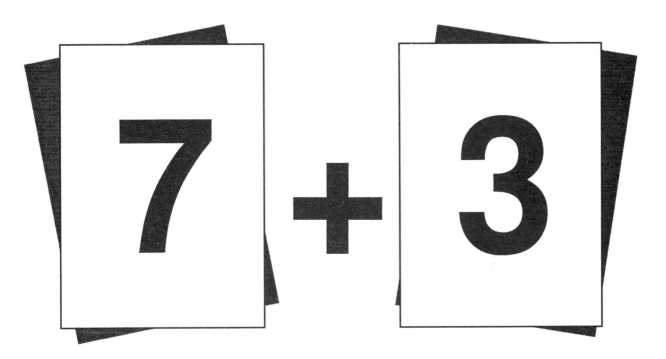

Procedure: (a) Each player has one set of the cards 1 to 9. Each chooses a number from 2 to 18 inclusive. The cards are shuffled and held face down.

In turn each player turns over one card and places it face up on the table so that two piles are placed side by side. When ever the sum of the two cards in view is the same as that chosen by one of the players he or she may claim all the cards on the table and adds them to the bottom of the remaining cards in his/her hand.

If all the cards go down without either of the player's chosen total occurring the players retrieve their piles, shuffle them and play again as before until one player eventually has all the cards in his/her hand.

Play can continue even when one of the players has exposed all his/her cards, the one with any cards continuing to turn over one of his/her remaining cards and placing alongside the other's last card.

Both players have to check every combination that appears thus busily practising the addition bonds to 18 thoroughly.

(b) Use cards marked 0 to 8 for subtraction. The players must each choose a 'target' number between 0 and 8. The smaller number on view is always subtracted from the larger.

Game 53   Puzzle pics I

Objective: Practice in addition and subtraction to 20.

Number of participants: One.

Materials: Puzzle picture sheets as here; coloured crayons.

Procedure: Read the colouring instructions with the child if necessary.

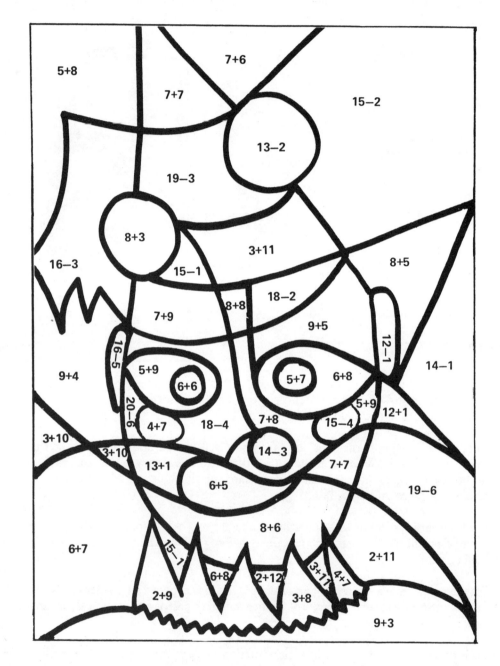

'Colour the shapes that make 11 red. Colour the shapes that make 12 blue. Colour all the 13's black. Leave 14 white. 15 is green, and 16 is yellow. Who is there when you have finished?'

Game 54   12, 13, 14 and 15    Game 58

Objective: To practise the composition of numbers from 12 to 15, using variations of three numerals.

Number of participants: One or groups working as individuals.

Materials: Base card, numeral cards 1 to 8 — one set for each player; stop clock if desired.

Procedure: 'You have to place the numbers round the sides of the square so that each side adds up to 12 (or 13, or 14, or 15).'

       For beginners the task is made easier by positioning two or more of the corner figures for the child.

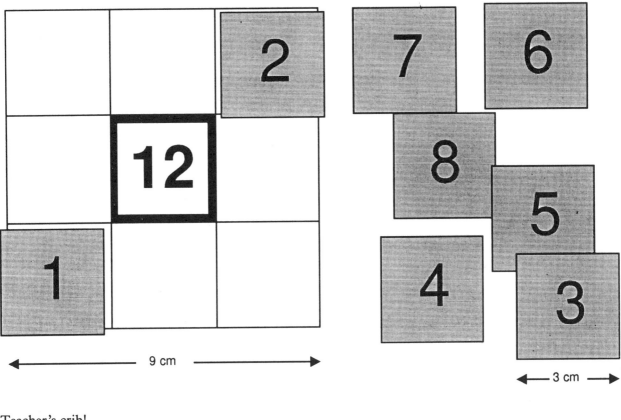

Teacher's crib!

6	4	2
5	12	7
1	8	3

2	3	8
6	13	4
5	7	1

7	6	1
3	14	5
4	2	8

3	5	7
4	15	2
8	1	6

Game 55   Find the twenties

Objective: To practise combining two numbers to total 20.

Number of participants: Two.

Materials: Use the circle below. Each player has a crayon of his/her own colour.

Procedure: i.   Each player in turn identifies two numbers totalling 20 and joins them with a line using his/her crayon.

ii.   The other player checks the addition before having his/her turn.

iii.   The winner is the player with the most correct linking pairs.

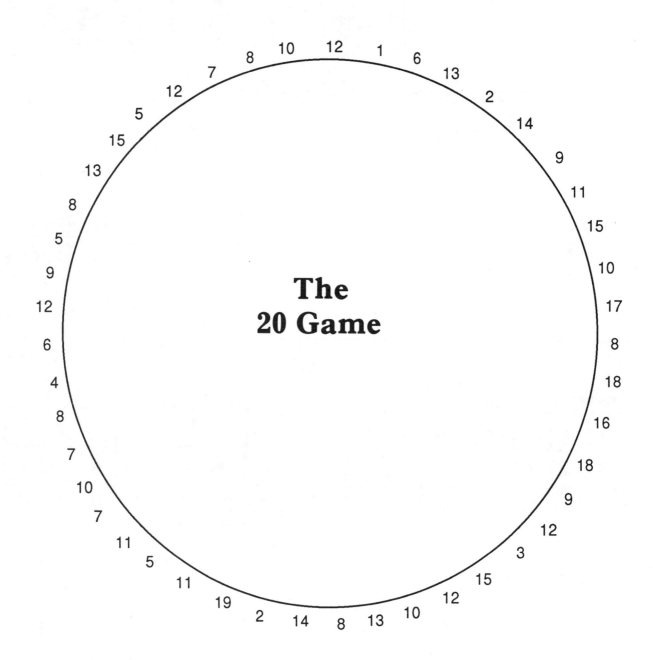

Game 56   Missing numbers II

Objective: To practise and quicken recognition of number bonds from 10 to 19. (follow-up to **Missing numbers I**, Game 27)

Number of participants: One.

Materials: A separate card, as illustrated, for each number from 10 to 19. Each circle in the inner ring is left blank. A loose counter is placed on each circle and the corresponding numeral written on each one.

Procedure: As **Missing numbers I**, Game 27.

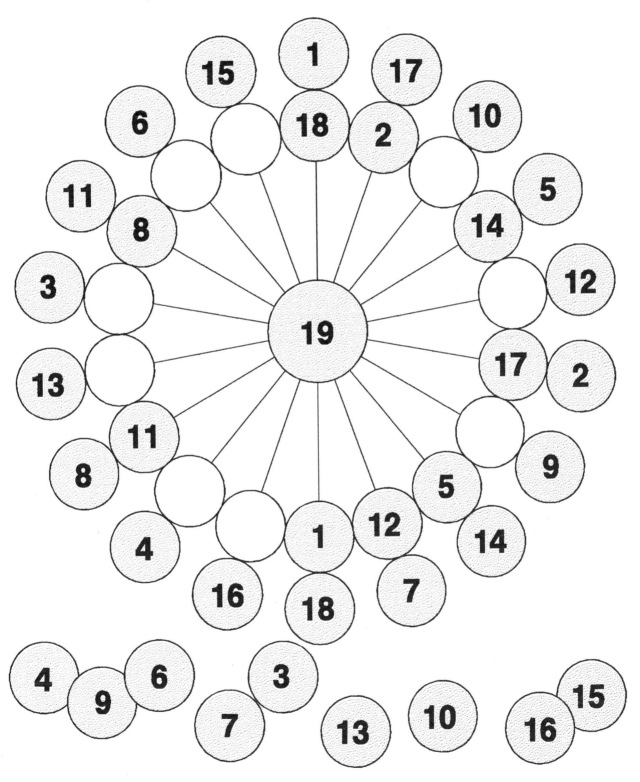

Game 57   Magic triangles II

Objective: A more difficult game to practise number combinations to 20.

Number of participants: Individual.

Materials: Triangle on card as illustrated. Cards 1 to 9 to fit spaces on triangle.

Procedure: "Make each side add up to 20". The task is made easier by placing 5 or 6 or 4 at the apex square and telling the child(ren) that the three corners must add up to 15. Try it yourself!

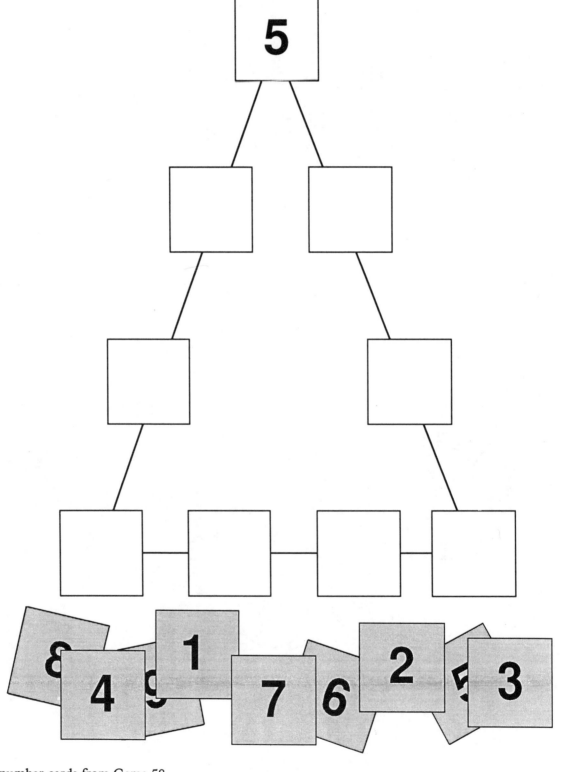

Use number cards from Game 58.

Game 58   Fifteens

Objective: A 'noughts and crosses' type game; the three numbers to total 15.

Number of participants: Two.

Materials: A 3 × 3 grid, nine cards numbered 1 to 9.

Procedure: One player has the even cards, the other the odd numbered ones. Odd starts by placing one of his/her five cards on the square of his/her choosing, followed by Even. The first player to complete a horizontal, vertical or diagonal line of three numbers that total 15 is the winner.

1	2	3	4	5
6	7	8	9	

Paste on to card and cut out.

Game 59   Ahmed's papers

Objective: Addition of numerals to totals of between 20 and 30.

Number of participants: Individual.

Materials: Worksheet as illustrated. Coloured crayons (for marking different routes.)

Procedure: "Every morning Ahmed has to deliver parcels of newspapers to newsagents in Lowtown, Manton and Kirby. He picks up the papers at Boomtown station. He wants to go the shortest way to save petrol. Which way do you think he should go?"

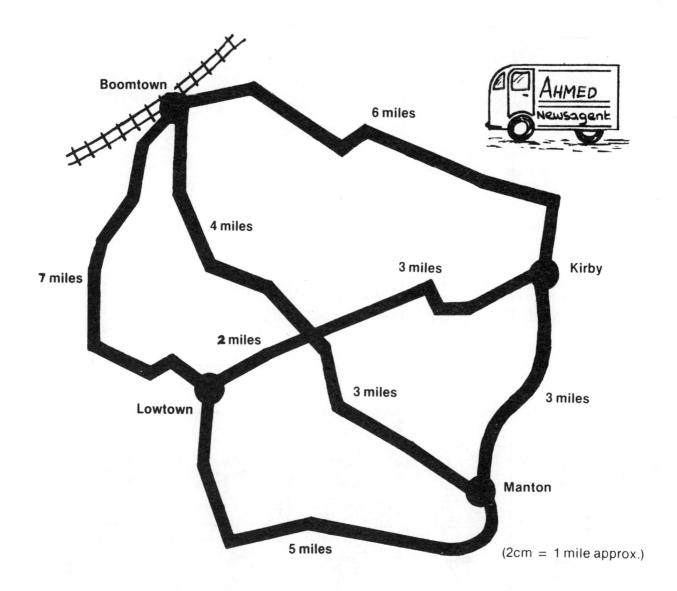

Boomtown

6 miles

4 miles

3 miles   Kirby

7 miles

2 miles

3 miles   3 miles

Lowtown

Manton

5 miles   (2cm = 1 mile approx.)

Game 60   Up the pyramid!

Objective: Addition of 9 numerals to form totals of between 16 and 28.

Number of participants: Individual children.

Materials: Worksheets as illustrated. Variation as appropriate.

Procedure: "There are lots of ways to the top of the pyramid." (There are 84!). "The way with the lowest total is the easiest. Can you find it?"

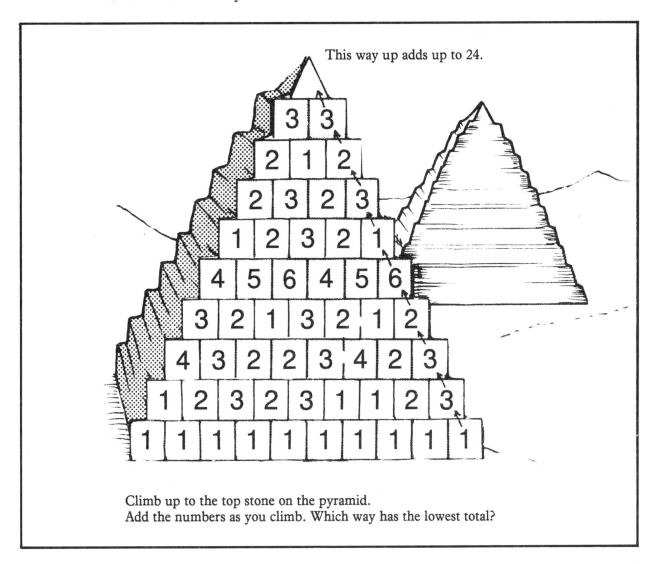

This way up adds up to 24.

Climb up to the top stone on the pyramid.
Add the numbers as you climb. Which way has the lowest total?

Clearly, it would depend on the child's abilities and needs whether or not you would insist on their finding and working all the possible 'sums'; or indeed if you would present a child with such a large pyramid. For starters, try the top three layers only (beginning at 2, 3, 2, 3) and gradually present larger pyramids as the child's facility improves.

Game 61 Pairs

Objective: To practise addition facts up to 20, including zero.

Number of participants: Two.

Materials: One calculator each. Two sets of cards numbered 0 to 20. 1 card labelled with various 'totals' e.g. 12, 15, 16, 19, 20. Scoring device.

Procedure: Place shuffled cards face down on the table. Each player takes it in turn to pick up 2 cards.

The cards numbered 0 to 20 should be shuffled and placed face down on the table. Each player takes it in turn to pick up 2 cards. Add using calculator. If the pair forms one of the required totals, place it by the total card, and replace with two new cards from the pile. If a total cannot be reached, take one further card each. In subsequent turns exchange one card from the hand for one in the pack, keeping a maximum of three cards at any time. The person with the most matched totals wins the game.

Game 62 One or two?

Objective: To practise subtraction. To develop logical thinking.

Number of participants: Two.

Materials: One calculator.

Procedure: First player enters 22. Each player then takes it in turn to enter 'minus' followed by the number '1' or '2' and '=', until zero appears to win.

(Strategy: The first player to reach 21, 18, 15, 12, 9, 6, 3 and thus 0 must be the winner.)

Variation: Vary the start numbers and the numbers to be subtracted.

Game 63 Down to the coach!

Objective: Addition of four numerals with totals up to 20.

Number of participants: Individual children.

Materials: Worksheets as illustrated. Variations as appropriate. A calculator.

Procedure: "There are six ways down the mountain to the coach. The way with the lowest total is the easiest. Which one is it?"

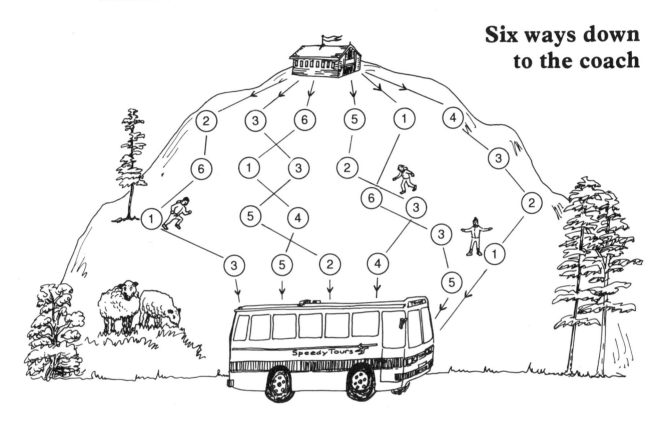

Six ways down to the coach

Game 64 Building Up

Objective: To complete building totals from 12 to 20 having initially used the score from two dice.

Number of participants: Two.

Materials: Three cards of each number from 12 to 20.
Two dice.

Procedure:

    i.   Shuffle cards and pile face down.

    ii.   First player turns over top card and then throws both dice:

    iii.   Calls out the number to bring the total of scores on the dice to the number on the card (in the following instance the correct answer would be 9)

 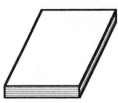 

    iv.   The second player checks the answer on the calculator.

    v.   Reverse roles, keeping scores using a scoring system.

Variation: Depending upon the ability of the players, make use of a watch with a seconds indicator and impose time limit of 5 or 10 seconds.

Game 65   Ways with tables

Objective: To make use of 2 to 5 times tables in novel settings.

Number of participants: Individuals or a group.

Materials: 'Pictures' as illustrated: pencils (coloured pencils if desired.)

Procedure: Present these tables series pictures, one at a time or several according to the child's ability. 'Can you fill in the missing numbers to finish the drawing?' Prompt as necessary.

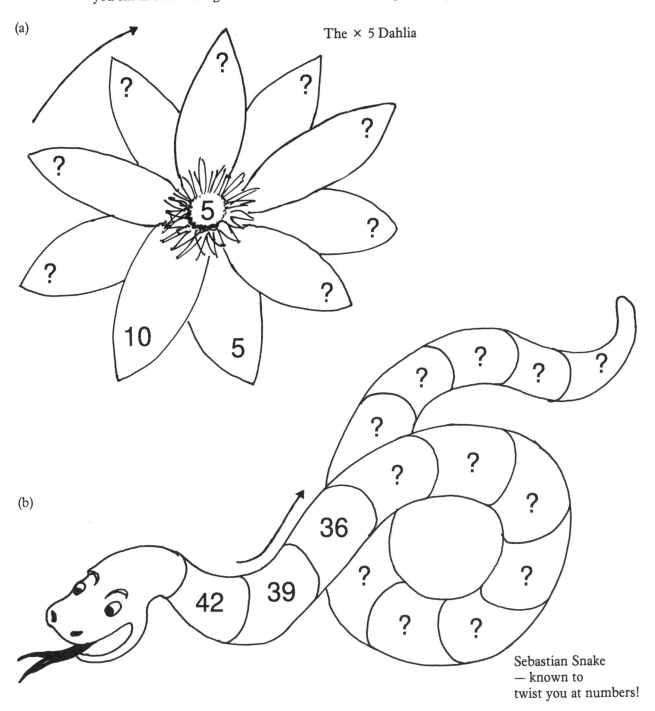

It is important that children acquire the skill of counting backwards (subtracting) hence this example. It is also important that they understand 'tables' exist beyond × 10 or × 12.

Eventually, children should realise that 'tables' proceed to infinity. Sebastian Snake is capable of tremendous growth.

(c)

(d)

Sam Trout, the × 4 fish.

Game 66   Round the clock

Objective: To introduce a speed element into the learning of 4 times, and other, tables.

Number of participants: One.

Materials: A card as illustrated: answer cards; a stop clock.

Procedure: This activity can be used to consolidate tables half-remembered. Place the 'clock' card and answer cards in front of the child. Demonstrate the activity with (in this case) 1 × 4 and 2 × 4. Take off these answers and say 'See how quickly you can put all the answer cards in their right places. Are you ready? Go!' Start the stop clock.

Record the time when the child finishes.

Repeat. Almost inevitably the child will improve his or her time and so receive a pleasant fillip. The activity can be repeated two or three times — as often as the child usefully can tolerate the activity. It is drill in disguise.

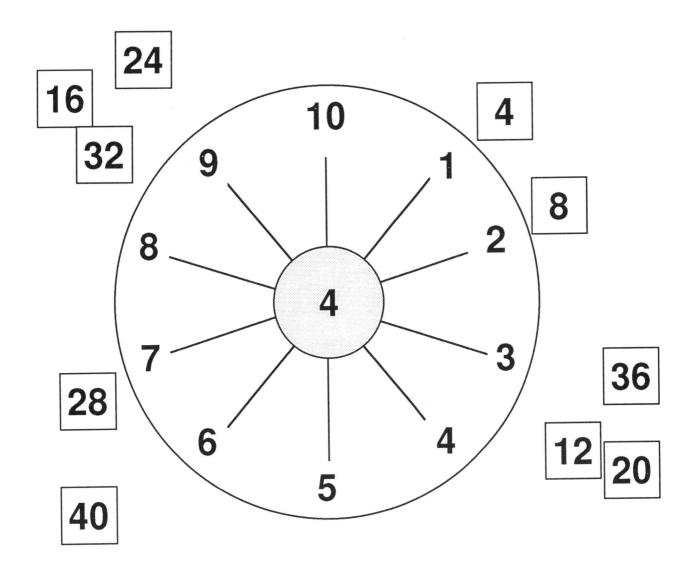

A more difficult version has the numbers round the 'clock' face in random order so two elements have to be sorted: the perimeter numbers and answers.

No Gamesheet has been prepared as the number cards will vary according to the table being practised.

Game 67   The way to the gold

Objective: To make use of 2 times table, in differentiating odds and evens to make progress in game. Subsequently to make use of other tables in a similar context.

Number of participants: One.

Materials: Activity sheet as illustrated; pen or pencil.

Procedure: *Stage 1:* Say 'There is a secret way to the gold. Can you find it? You can move on from 'start' one square at a time to a square where the number there can be divided exactly by 2. Mark the path you take by writing a X on each square you go on.'

23	2	1	7	12	11	17
18	21	20	16	27	24	9
14	13	25	29	31	33	30
11	8	19	gold	15	38	13
6	9	17	22	35	42	43
4	1	7	26	5	47	48
3	START ↑	5	19	36	54	45

Movement may be horizontally, vertically or diagonally but only one square at a time.

Stage 2: A 'track' may be devised so that movement may be to any square whose number is divisible by 2 or 3 (or both), or any other two factors.

84

Stage 3: Here is a 'track' where movement may be made to any square whose number is divisible by 2, 3 or 5. Note: Use directions appropriate to your particular child.

239	174	207	259	211	181	193	180	130	163	161
162	227	173	201	221	203	164	157	151	96	137
196	223	233	257	148	117	187	143	139	75	71
263	177	311	281	191	11	193	169	103	133	51
317	209	246	257	19	41	17	131	109	123	113
313	211	280	329	61	Gold	121	119	112	101	107
307	258	271	79	73	9	97	98	91	79	103
331	279	277	243	81	79	87	47	42	71	73
307	323	285	61	59	49	~~8~~	41	53	36	67
109	313	13	11	7	~~6~~	37	~~16~~	97	59	27
329	281	17	Start ↑	~~10~~	23	19	43	~~36~~	18	61

etc.

This kind of activity and presentation is adaptable for all the multiplication tables and can be graded in difficulty by size of grid and by the dimension of the numbers used. In short the idea can be made to fit each child's needs.

The target can be varied from finding a 'track' with factors to, say, a 'track' formed from prime numbers.

Game 68   Bugs' legs

Objective: Identifying the factors of numbers up to 20.

Number of participants: One.

Materials: Prepared sheets as below (A4 size); pencils; tables square if desired or if necessary, coloured crayons.

Procedure: 'Number bugs are strange creatures. Each bug has a leg for each "times" sum which will make its number. You have to draw the bug a leg for each sum. Bug Ten has four legs.

Give the other Number bugs the right number of legs.'

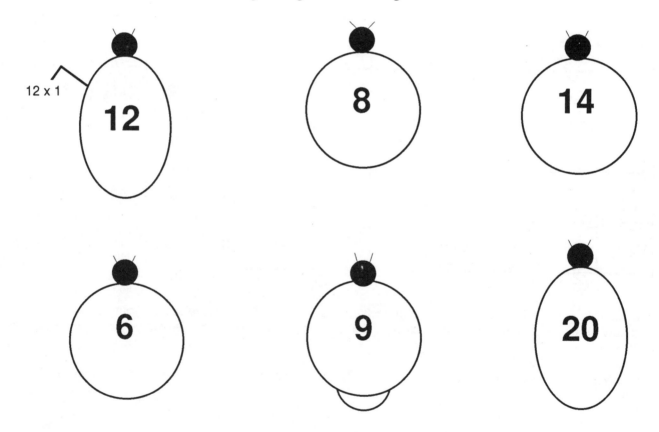

'When you have finished the sheet, colour your bugs.'

Note: In these sketches, the size of the 'Bug' suggests the number of factors — which sometimes helps the children. Draw the 'Bugs' identically if you wish.

86

Game 69   Balloon man

Objective: To make use of 2 to 5 times tables for simple division tasks.

Number of participants: Individuals.

Materials: Prepared sheets as illustrated; coloured crayons.

Procedure: See the instructions on the drawing (below).

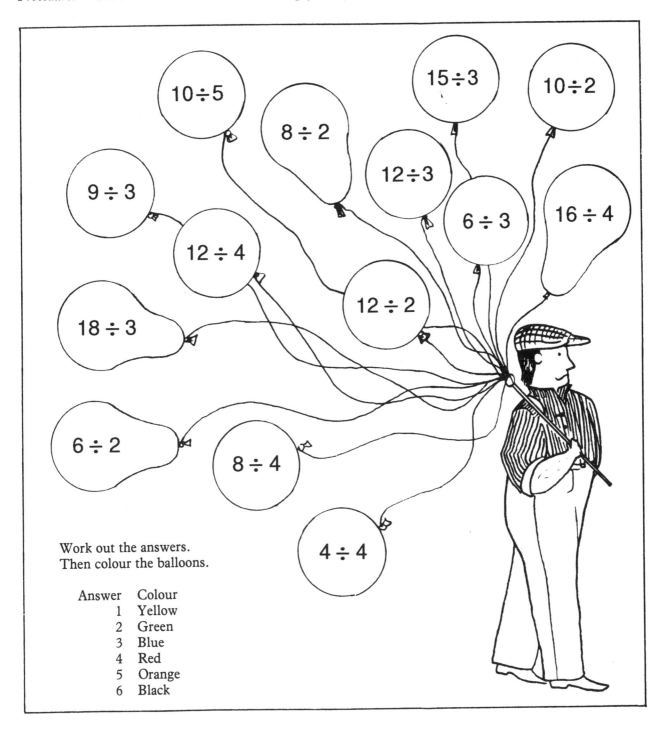

Work out the answers.
Then colour the balloons.

Answer	Colour
1	Yellow
2	Green
3	Blue
4	Red
5	Orange
6	Black

Game 70   Triangle teasers

Objective: To make use of 2 to 5 times tables to determine the factors of a given product.

Number of participants: Individuals.

Materials: Prepared sheets of puzzles as below. Paper and pencil.

Procedure: 1. 'Can you work out how we get the big numbers in the triangles? Use the small figures.'

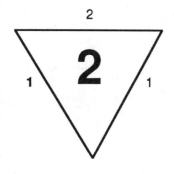 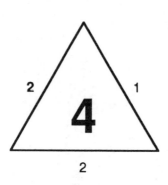 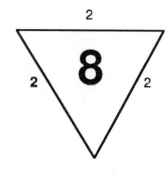

2. 'Now, can you put the correct little numbers round these triangles? You have to follow the pattern you have discovered — but now it's the other way round!'

(a) 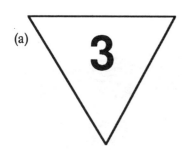 (b) 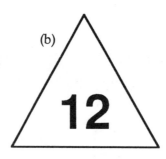 (c)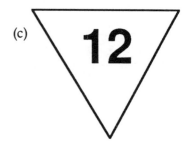

(d) 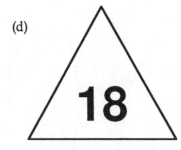 (e)  (f)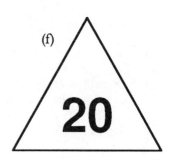

(g) 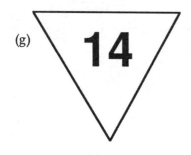 (h) 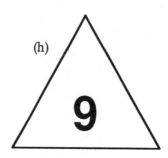 (i)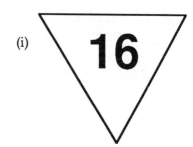

88

Game 71   Pigeon Holes   Gamesheet 16

Objective: To classify numbers from 1 — 30 on a matrix by the following criteria: factors of 12; prime numbers; multiples of 3 or 5; odd or even numbers.

Number of participants: One up to four.

Materials: A 5 × 5 grid on a board, number cards labelled 1 to 30, labelling cards (or number descriptions written on the margin of the card).

Procedure: If one player, the number cards are spread out face up and he or she takes one at a time and tries to place it on the grid so that it accords with the column and/or row description. Lots of thinking and reasoning!

If two or more players, the number cards are shuffled and dealt. Then the players take turns to place their cards on the grid appropriately. When all the spaces that can be used are occupied the players' remaining cards are separately added. The player with the lowest total wins, so there is encouragement to use the larger numbers.

Variation: The labelling cards can be varied and variously placed. The size of the grid can be increased, and larger numbers used.

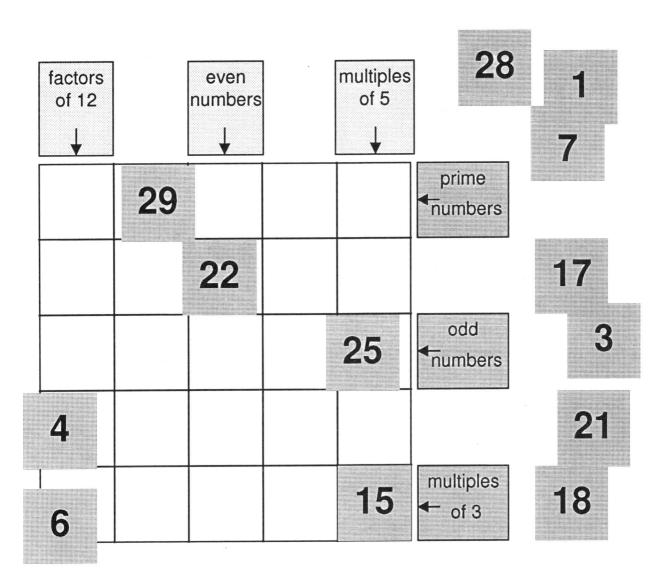

89

Game 72 Flash game

Objective: To practise the four basic processes, introducing a speed element.

Number of participants: Two.

Materials: Calculator. Set of cards with simple sums commensurate with pupils' abilities. (e.g. 3 × 5, 5 + 4 etc.)

Procedure: i.   Place cards face down in pile.

               ii.   Pupil without calculator turns over top card. He/she then attempts to call out the answer before the other pupil can key the sum into the calculator and obtain the answer in that way.

               iii.   Use scoring device to indicate first pupil to obtain the correct answer.

Note: This game provides splendid practise both in the speed and accuracy of keying as well as speed in the recall of simple number facts.

Game 73 One to twenty

Objective: To use addition, subtraction and multiplication processes to make a given number.

Number of participants: Individual, though much useful discussion is generated if pupils work in pairs, non-competitively.

Materials: Calculator. Pencil and paper.

Procedure: Using keys 3, 4, +, and − and × only on the calculator, obtain processes for every number from 1 to 20. (e.g. 1 = 4 − 3, 2 = 3 + 3 − 4 etc.). Record results.

Variations: Once confidence has been established, pupils can be invited to experiment, using different start numbers and introducing the ÷ key.

Game 74   **Fill the space** Gamesheet 17

Objective: To determine the unknown when two of *input/function/output* are given in sums with totals not exceeding 20.

Materials: Large number of cards approx 8cm × 3cm with one unknown in sums with totals not exceeding 20.

e.g.

20 - ☐ = 11	11 ☐ 8 = 19	14 - ☐ = 10
7 + ☐ = 9	12 ÷ 2 = ☐	☐ ÷ 2 = 9
☐ x 6 = 18	8 + ☐ = 19	5 ☐ 3 = 15

Watch with second indicator. One calculator.

Procedure:

     i.   Shuffle cards and place face downwards in pile.

     ii.   First player turns top card and, timed by second player, is allowed a given number of seconds to call the correct answer. Second player checks answer with calculator.

OR   iii.   Both players work simultneously from upturned card. The first to call correctly is the winner. No score (or forfeit one point) if incorrect.

OR   iv.   As ii above. Apply a forfeit of 10 seconds if answer is not given within 10 seconds or is incorrect. To score in this version, note number of seconds from turning card to calling answer. Winner is player with the lowest score after a given number of turns.

Game 75   Digits   Gamesheet 18

Objective: To familiarise pupils with digital display numbers.

Number of participants: Individual.

Materials: Photocopied sheets with 10 blank digital frames. Card or matchstick bars in contrasting colour.

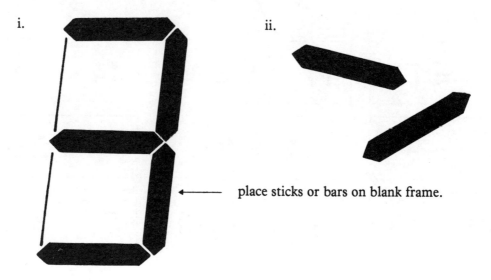

i.

ii.

← place sticks or bars on blank frame.

Procedure: i.   Pupil builds up all digits from 0 to 9, checking response with calculator.

                ii.   Pupil writes normal form of numeral at the side of each digit.

Game 76   3 in a row   **Gamesheet 4**

Objective: To familiarise pupils with the positions of the numbers on the keyboard.

Number of participants: Two.

Materials: 2 copies of calculator keyboard. 4 sets of cards numbered 1 to 9. Two pencils.

Procedure: Shuffle cards and place face down in a pile in the middle of the table. In turns take one card from the pack and cross off the appropriate number on the keyboard. The first player to get 3 crosses in a row/column/diagonal wins.

Game 77   **Keyboard snap**   **Gamesheet 4**

Objective: To familiarise pupils with the positions of the numbers on the keyboard.

Number of participants: Two.

Materials: Copy of calculator keyboard, 4 sets of cards numbered 1 to 9.

Procedure: Deal 9 cards face-down to each player who arranges them in a 3 × 3 square. Take turns to expose one card at a time in the same order as the keyboard, starting with position 1, then position 2 etc. If the card matches the number, shout 'snap' to win. If no winner, reshuffle cards and start again.

7	8	9
4	5	6
1	2	3

9 ← Last card to be exposed.

First card to be exposed. → 1

93

Game 78 ◈ Guess the score

Objective: To provide practise in using calculator keys.

Number of participants: Two.

Materials: One calculator. Two dice. Pen and paper.

Procedure:

    i.   One pupil throws 2 dice secretly and notes scores on paper in the order thrown. e.g. 4 3.

    ii.   He or she enters the first score on calculator.

Enter first score		4

    iii.   Second pupil takes calculator

Multiply by 5	× 5	20
Add 3	+ 3	23
Multiply by 2	× 2	46

    iv.   First pupil takes calculator

Adds score of second die	+ second score	49
Subtract 6	− 6	43
Answer is 2 scores of die in correct order		43

Game 79 ◈ Working the number

Objective: To provide practise in accurate keying.

Number of participants: Two.

Materials: One calculator for each participant. Pencil and paper. Copy of rules unless teacher led.

Procedure: Teacher asks both pupils to think of any number with 3 or 4 digits (e.g. 1992) and to write it down secretly.

    i.   Both pupils enter their number into the calculator.

		e.g. 1992

    ii.

Double it.	× 2	3984
Add 4.	+ 4	3988
Divide by 2.	÷ 2	1994
Add 7.	+ 7	2001
Multiply by 8.	× 8	16008
Subtract 12.	− 12	15996
Divide by 4.	÷ 4	3999
Subtract 11.	− 11	3988

    iii.   Swap calculators

    iv.

Subtract 4.	− 4	3984
Divide by 2.	÷ 2	1992

The calculator should indicate the partners original number. If it does not do so, pupils rework the procedure together.

Game 80 Date of birth

Objective: To practise accuracy in selecting the correct keys of a calculator.

Number of participants: One or more (or whole class)

Materials: One calculator for each participant.

Procedure:

i. Establish that participants know their date of birth in numerical form
e.g. 9 July 1983 = 9/7/83

ii.

Enter day of month on which born e.g.	9	9
Multiply by 20	× 20	180
Add 3	+ 3	183
Multiply by 5	× 5	915
Add number of month born e.g. 7	+ 7	922
Multiply by 20	× 20	18440
Add 3	+ 3	18443
Multiply by 5	× 5	92215
Add last 2 digits of year born	+ 83	92298
Subtract 1515	− 1515	90783
Answer is date of birth		9.7.83

Game 81 Magic 6

Objective: To provide practise in using the keys. To follow instructions.

Number of participants: One or more (or whole class).

Materials: One calculator for each participant. Pen and paper.

Procedure:

i. On paper, each participant writes down any number with up to 4 digits. Add 1 to this number and write answer underneath. Add 1 more to this number and write answer underneath.

ii. Enter original number into calculator

e.g. 1992

iii. Add second number   e.g. 1993   3985

iv. Add third number   e.g. 1994   5979

v. Add 15   + 15   5994

vi. Divide by 3   ÷ 3   1998

vii. Subtract original number   − 1992   6

Answer is always 6.

Game 82 Magic 9

Objective: To practise ordering numbers. To add up to 4 single digits.

Number of participants: One or more (up to whole class).

Materials: One calculator each. Pen and paper.

Procedure:

i.	Write down a 4 digit number containing different digits.	e.g. 2834
ii.	Jumble up the digits to form a new number	e.g. 3842
iii.	Enter larger number on calculator	3842
iv.	Subtract smaller number	− 2834
v.	Write down answer and clear calculator	1008
vi.	On calculator, add individual digits of previous answer	9
vii.	If the answer has more than one digit, write them down, clear the calculator then add these digits.	

The answer is always 9.

Game 83 Magic 13

Objective: To practise using the keys of a calculator. To follow instructions precisely.

Number of participants: One or more (or whole class).

Materials: One calculator for each participant. Pen and paper.

Procedure:

i.	Write down any 3 digit number		e.g. 260
ii.	Enter it twice into calculator		260260
iii.	Divide by 7		37180
iv.	Divide by original 3 digit number e.g. 260	÷ 260	143
v.	Divide by 11	÷ 11	13
vi.	Press =		

Answer is always 13.

Game 84   Magic 37

Objective: To practise using the keys of a calculator. To practise addition of 3 numbers less than 10.

Number of participants: One or more (up to whole class).

Materials: One calculator each. Pack of cards numbered 1 to 9 each. Paper and pencil.

Procedure:

i.	The pupil picks card from pile.	e.g. 8
ii.	On calculator, enter this number and multiply by 111.	888
iii.	In head (or on paper) add digits of the result. e.g. 8 + 8 + 8 = 24	24
iv.	On calculator divide by this result. e.g. 888 ÷ 24	37

The answer is always 37.

Level 4

Addition and subtraction to 100.

Learning multiplication facts up to 10 × 10 - and beyond.

Calculator games marked

Game 85   Frame the 100's

Objective: To practise addition of four numbers to form totals of 100.

Number of participants: Individual, or a group working as individuals.

Materials: A sheet of numbers on a grid as illustrated. Coloured pencils; 'Window' cards to frame four squares.

Procedure: (see **Frame the 10's**, Game 29.) Read the rubric in the grid with the pupil. Help her/him to find the first 100 square and show how to draw a line round it with a crayon. The pupil uses a different coloured crayon for each '100' identified.

The four numbers in the black square add up to 100.

There are seven more lots of four numbers that will add up to 100. Find them.

Colour each large square of four numbers with a different colour.

Note:
You may use the numbers more than once.

25	44	6	13	24
13	18	45	36	27
43	26	34	29	19
19	47	27	10	35
20	14	25	38	17

Game 86   Coding names

Objective: To provide addition practice, based on coded names. Most totals, using the code suggested, will be less than 100.

Number of participants: Individuals or groups.

Materials: Paper and pencil for each child; a list of children's names.

Procedure: Write up a simple alphabet 'code':

JOHN

Aa	Bb	Cc	Dd	Ee	Ff	Gg	Hh	Ii
1	2	3	4	5	6	7	8	9

ALI

Janet

Jj	Kk	Ll	Mm	Nn	Oo	Pp	Qq	Rr
10	11	12	13	14	15	16	17	18

Karen

Ss	Tt	Uu	Vv	Ww	Xx	Yy	Zz
19	20	21	22	23	24	25	26

BILL

'Change your name into numbers:

R	o	y
18	15	25

Timothy Add the numbers: 18 + 15 + 25 = 58.

Benny   Do the same for the other children's names (or some of the others' names).

MARY

Eg.	S	t	e	v	e	n		
	19	20	5	22	5	14	=	85

Jagdish

S	u	s	a	n		
19	21	19	1	14	=	74

Catherine

D	a	v	i	d		
4	1	22	9	4	=	40

WESLEY

J	a	c	k	i	e		
10	1	3	11	9	5	=	39

Anne

EDWARD

Who's name has the largest total?
Put the names in order according to their 'code' totals.
(Note: a short name can produce a large total.)

Development: If you wish the children to practise larger 'sums' add the surnames.
So, for example, a name like Dewdrop Drainpipe would produce:

4 + 5 + 23 + 4 + 18 + 15 + 16 Dewdrop and
4 + 18 + 1 + 9 + 14 + 16 + 9 + 16 + 5 Drainpipe.

Another variation is to use the names of pop stars or soccer players or soccer clubs. They all serve to sugar the pill!

Game 87 Wheelies II Gamesheet 8

Objectives: i.   Addition of 2 two-digit numbers involving totals up to 100.

ii.   Subtraction using 2 two-digit numbers of less than 50, avoiding decomposition.

Number of participants: Individual.

Materials: As **Wheelies I**, Game 30, but with numerals as below.

Procedure: Pupils rotate wheel to produce a total of 88 addition and 88 subtraction tasks. There is an obvious necessity for selectivity on the part of the teacher, determining limits on the basis of individual need.

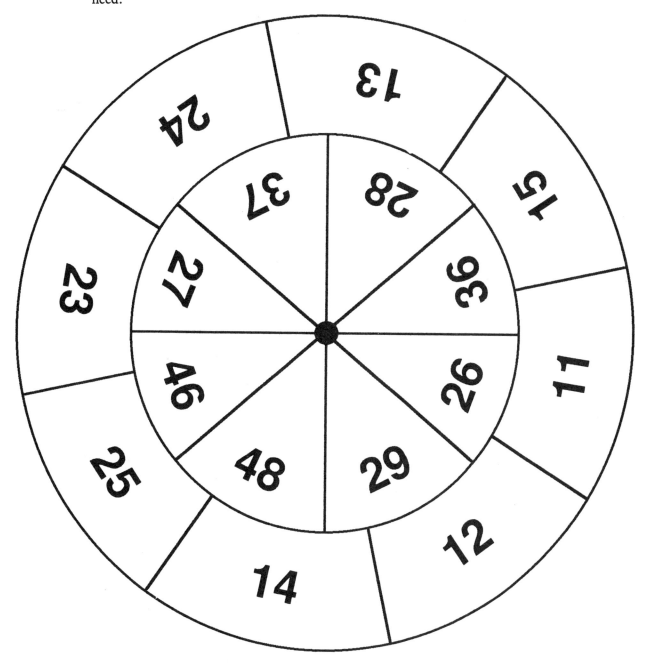

In the above example, when used for subtraction, decomposition and exchange are avoided by having larger or equal digits in both places (tens and units) on the inside wheel.

Using the device the number of problems is also governed by the number of sectors you draw on the wheels. The work load, quantity and difficulty, for each child must be decided by your judgement of the 'challenge' level for him.

Game 88   Going for gold

Objective: To practise the application of all four basic processes within the range of 1 — 36.

Number of participants: Two, but possible with three or four.

Materials: A numbered, squared board as illustrated, 16 red counters and 16 yellow, two dice (1 to 6), pencil and paper.

Procedure: In turn each player rolls the dice and tries hard to add, subtract, multiply or divide the two numbers shown to make a number in one of the vacant squares. If none is available the other player tries.

Scoring: for each square covered one point is scored. If the square attained adjoins a 'gold' square a bonus point is added to the player's tally. In the case of '18', four bonus points are added since that square adjoins four 'gold' squares, '4' earns two bonus points, but '16' none.

SCORE	
RED	**YELLOW**
bonus	bonus
1	1 + 2
1 + 4	1
1	1 + 1

← 20 cm →

3	0	GOLD	9	6
7	GOLD	18	GOLD	1
2	10	GOLD	4	16
15	12	8	11	5

16 cm

The player with the highest total of points after, say, 30 rolls of the dice is the winner whether or not the squares are all covered. (To play until all the squares are covered might lead to boredom for young players.)

The next stage is to enlarge the board gradually and then to introduce a third die and the use of brackets in the calculation: e.g. $5 + 2 + 6 = 13$, $(5 + 2) - 6 = 1$. $(5 - 2) + 6 = 9$, $(6 - 5) + 2 = 3$, $(6 \times 5) \div 2 = 15$, etc.

Game 89   Say 99 - and 1089!

Objectives: To present arithmetical curiosities involving addition and subtraction of:

  i.   two-digit numbers.
  ii. three-digit numbers.

Number of participants: One or several.

Materials: Paper and pencil.

Procedure: (a) *Two-figure amounts*
1. Write down any number with tens and units in it, say 13. (The digits *must* be different from one another.)

2. Now write down the number you get if you turn 13 back to front (reverse it). You get 31.

3. Take the smaller number (13) from the larger (31):

$$\begin{array}{r} 31 \\ -13 \\ \hline 18 \end{array}$$

4. Use the figures from this number (18). Write this answer back to front: 81.

5. Add this new number (81) to the first answer (18):

$$\begin{array}{r} 81 \\ +18 \\ \hline 99 \end{array}$$

6. Try this on ten more numbers. What is the answer?

(b) *Three-figure amounts*
1. Similar to (a). Write down any number with hundreds, tens and units in it. All the figures *must* be different.
Let's say the number is 123.

2. Now reverse the number: 321.

3. Take the smaller from the larger:

$$\begin{array}{r} 321 \\ -123 \\ \hline 198 \end{array}$$

4. Now reverse that first answer: 198 becomes 891.

5. Add this to your first answer:

$$\begin{array}{r} 198 \\ +891 \\ \hline 1089 \end{array}$$

6. Try it on ten more numbers. Again, what is the answer?

Go on ... does the same thing happen with four-digit numbers?

Game 90 Discovery

Objective: To practise the four basic rules. To encourage problem solving strategies.

Number of participants: One or more.

Materials: One calculator, Pen and paper.

Procedure: Using the keys +, −, × and ÷ make as many different sums as possible which give the answer 99 (or any other number.)

Game 91 Selection   Gamesheet 4

Objective: To practise the four basic rules. To provide opportunities to develop concepts and make comparisons.

Number of participants: One or more.

Materials: One calculator. Pen and paper. Set of cards numbered 0 to 9.

Procedure: Child selects three cards from the set and makes as many sums as possible on the calculator using the four basic rules.

Game 92 Products   Gamesheet 4

Objectives: To practise multiplication facts of numbers less than 10. To provide opportunities for comparison of size.

Number of participants: One or more.

Materials: One calculator. Set of cards from 1 to 9.

Procedure: Child picks three cards from pile, then selects the two which would give the largest product. Only the two number-keys and × and = may be used on the calculator.

Game 93 Multiples

Objective: To increase pupils understanding of place value to four figures.

Number of participants: Individual.

Materials: Pen and stout paper or thin card. Scissors. Set of cards.

4 x 2	2 x 400	20 x 40
2 x 4	200 x 4	40 x 20
4 x 20	4 x 200	
2 x 40	400 x 2	

Procedure:

   i. The set of cards is shuffled and piled face-down.

   ii. Player takes top card and writes whole sum, and answer, on paper, using calculator.

   iii. Player repeats process until all sums are completed. Cuts answer paper so that each sum is on a separate piece of paper.

   iv. Player asked to sort papers so that sums with identical answers are grouped. Player required to make observations on outcome.

Variation: Repeat whole procedure, using new cards substituting the addition sign in place of the multiplication sign. Invite comparison between the two sets of answers.

Repeat the whole, using two other digits.

Game 94 Magic Hexagons

Objective: To manipulate the numerals 1 to 19 within a hexagon to form a constant total (38).

Materials: The hexagon, as illustrated, with the given numbers inserted. The remainder of the numerals from 1 to 19 to be put on to smaller hexagonal cards to fit the spaces.

Procedure: "Try to arrange your cards on the empty spaces on the hexagon so that the vertical and diagonal lines all have the same total."

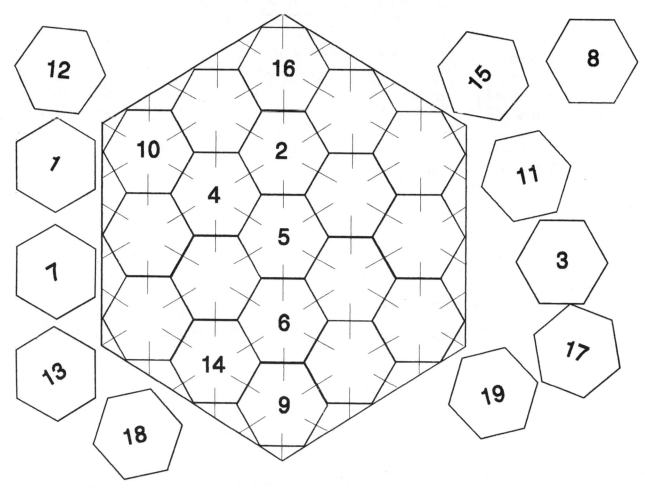

Note: Using the numbers inserted there is a strategy that removes the necessity for trial and error tactics. If the 4, 10 and 14 are removed however, trial and error tactics are likely to be necessary.

Use of the calculator for this game enables the player to concentrate on the strategies involved rather than on the mechanics involved in totalling 38.

Game 95   Making 36's

Objective: To identify all the factors of 36 in a context of forming patterns through the use of tables.

Number of participants: Individuals. Working in pairs can generate useful discussion.

Materials: Prepared sheets with circles whose circumferences are marked off every 10 degrees; coloured pencils; rulers. (Older pupils might draw their own circles.)

Procedure: It is probably easiest to begin with a square and the factors 4 × 9, but this is obviously a decision for the teacher.

'Choose a coloured pencil. Start at 0. Join 0 to 9. Use your ruler. Then join 9 to 18. Now join 18 to 27, and 27 to 36 (0). What shape is that? What table have you used?
1 × 9 = 9, 2 × 9 = 18, 3 × 9 = 27, and 4 × 9 = 36.'

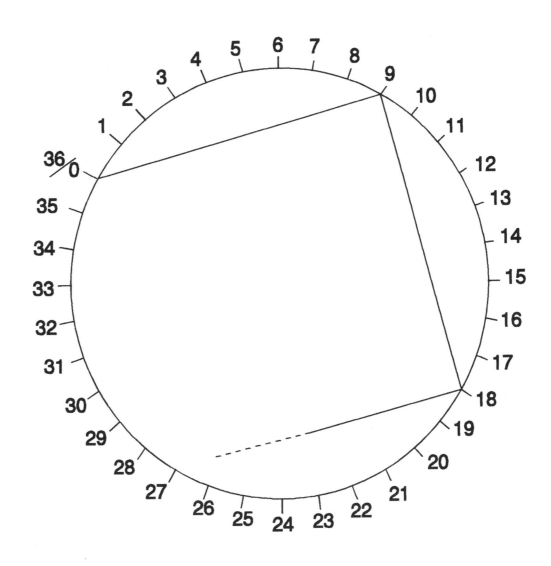

Incidentally it is important not to present shapes always standing 'four-square' on the page: hence the tilt in this illustration. At a later stage the children could enjoy drawing other, differently coloured squares starting on 1 (10, 19, 28, 1) then 2, etc.

The × 12 table (1 × 12 = 12, 2 × 12 = 24, 3 × 12 = 36) produces a triangle.

The × 6 table (1 × 6 = 6, 2 × 6 = 12, 3 × 6 = 18, 4 × 6 = 24, 5 × 6 = 30 and 6 × 6 = 36) gives a hexagon (6 sides).

The × 4 table (1 × 4 = 4, 2 × 4 = 8, 3 × 4 = 12, 4 × 4 = 16, 5 × 4 = 20, 6 × 4 = 24, 7 × 4 = 28, 8 × 4 = 32, 9 × 4 = 36) gives nonagon (9 sides).

The × 3 table (3, 6, 9 12, 15, 18, 21, 24, 27, 30, 33, 36) gives a duodecagon (12 sides); and the × 2 table (not shown in the illustration, below) would produce an 18-sided shape.

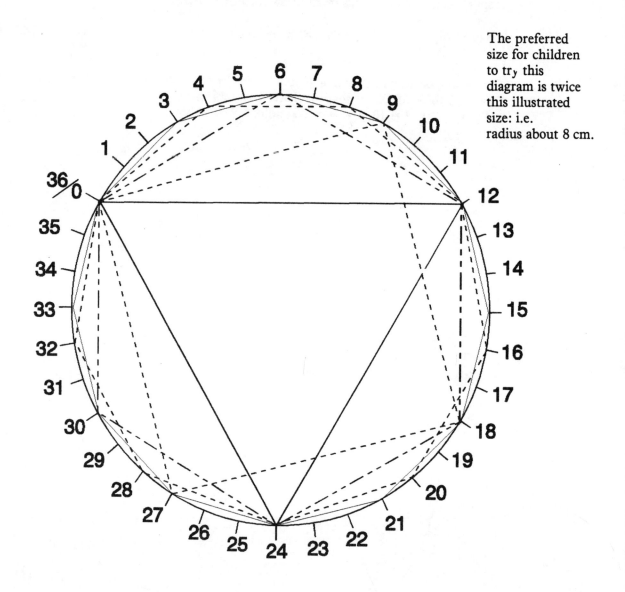

The preferred size for children to try this diagram is twice this illustrated size: i.e. radius about 8 cm.

—————————— — triangle from the × 12 table
– – – – – – – – — square from the × 9 table
– · —— – · —— — hexagon from the × 6 table
– · · – · · – · · — nonagon from the × 4 table
—————————— — duodecagon from the × 3 table

First, draw each shape in separate circles.
The combined shapes in one circle are for a grand finale.

Game 96   Cover up   Gamesheet 22

Game 1.

Objective: A bingo-type game to practice tables to products of 36. Mainly multiplication but some division.

Number of participants: Two (or possibly three or four with another board(s)).

Materials: Playing board as illustrated or the two players' halves may be separated if you don't trust them! For first game ignore/cover 7 and 11.

1	2	3			1	2	3
4	5	6	7		4	5	6
8	9	10	11	7	8	9	10
12	15	16		11	12	15	16
18	20	24			18	20	24
25	30	36			25	30	36

18 cm (vertical)
24 cm (horizontal)

18 counters (for first game) 20 (for second game) per player: two dice.

Procedure: The players roll a die to decide who starts. Higher begins. Each player in turn roll the two dice, works out the product of the two numbers showing and covers the corresponding number on his/her card. If a dividend is also possible, he or she may cover that number. For example, if the dice produce this

he or she covers 15 only (5 × 3) (5 − 3 leaves a remainder so no natural number answer). If the dice produce

he or she may cover 12 (6 × 2) and 3 (6 ÷ 2) if they are available. The player to cover all his or her numbers first wins, or if a deadline is necessary (some products can be elusive!) the player with the most numbers covered wins.

109

Game 2.
Objective: A variation of Game 1, using all the board numbers (including 7 and 11) to practise:
— multiplication (products to 36)
— subtraction (difference) and
— addition (sum)

Number of participants: Two (or up to four with another board).

Materials: As in previous game using all the board; 20 counters for each player (or pair).

Procedure: Players roll a die to decide who starts. Higher begins. Players then take it in turns to roll two dice. The player then covers the product, the difference and the sum of the two numbers showing on the dice if these answers are available on his board. For example, if the two dice produce this

the player may cover 15 (3 × 5), 2 (5 − 3) and 8 (3 + 5). If any of these answers are already covered the player covers those that are available and awaits his or her next turn.

Note: The low numbers in both these games are usually covered first and there is often a 'wastage' of answers as the game proceeds: i.e. 1, 2, 3, will occur in the answers many times more than is needed to get these numbers covered. Occasionally it will be necessary to declare a deadline. Then the player with the most numbers on his or her card covered wins.

Game 97   Marathon

Objective: To practice using tables up to 6 times 6 to obtain high cumulative totals on a number line.

Number of participants: Two.

Materials: A long number line (500 and up to 1,000 if possible) fastened flat along a window ledge or on the floor clear of other children as much as possible; counters: a pair of dice and a shaker.

Procedure: (a) The two players throw one die for turns: the higher goes first. The first player then throws both dice, multiplies the two numbers together and moves his or her counter on the amount of their product. Therefore the biggest move with orthodox dice will be 36 (6 × 6).

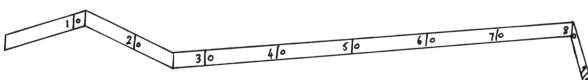

(b) For the higher numbers mark the dice (or one of them) 5, 6, 7, 8, 9 and 10 on their faces. Now the largest move forward will be 100 (10 × 10).

(c) To practise one table: choose a table, × 2 up to × 10, and use one die. Multiply the number on the die by 2, 3 or whichever table was chosen. So, if the × 6 table is the one.

 × 6 = 18.

and the player moves his or her counter on 18 places.

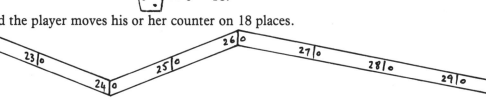

(d) The number can be periodically marked with 'bonus' or 'punishment' places (addition and subtraction) as in *Snakes and-Ladders*.

Dealing with large number 'concretely' and visually on a long number strip facilitates the move towards avoiding counting on in ones every time. So, for example, with a counter on 51 and 3 × 4 thrown with the dice, some children will be helped to move on quickly to 51 + 12 = 51 + 10 + 2 = 61 + 2 = 63.

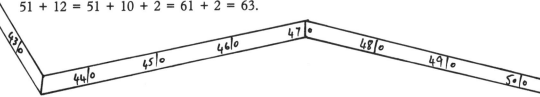

Game 98   Tables snap Gamesheet 23

Objective: To practice tables. The example shown is the 6 times table.

Number of participants: Two.

Materials: Two sets of ten cards made from thick manilla, or blank playing cards on which are written the multiplication facts for the table to be practised: e.g. 1 × 6, 2 × 6, 3 × 6, 4 × 6, 5 × 6, 6 × 6, 7 × 6, 8 × 6, 9 × 6, 10 × 6. (Twenty cards in these two sets). Two sets of 'answer' cards (same size) on which are written the sums of the multiplication facts from the first sets of cards; e.g. 6, 12, 18, 24, 30, 36, 42, 48, 54, 60 (twenty cards). So 40 cards altogether are needed.

'Answer' Cards   **'Fact' Cards**

Procedure: Separately shuffle the 'facts' cards and the 'answer' ones. Player A has the 'facts' and player B the 'answer' cards face down.

They take it in turn to place a card face up on the table, the second alongside the first, making two piles, shouting (calling?) "Snap!" in the usual way when the 'fact' card matches the 'answer' card. If correct the caller collects all the cards down and places them in one pile below the remaining cards he or she is holding.

At first 'facts' lie opposite 'answers' but as the cards become mixed in the course of the game the winning combinations can be, for example, 12 and 2 × 6, or 2 × 6 and 2 × 6, or 12 and 12.

The winner is the player who eventually has all the cards; or a time limit may be set and the winner is the player with most cards.

Game 99   Men from Mars

Objective: To practise the use of 6, 7 and 8 times tables.

Number of participants: Individual.

Materials: Illustrated sheet as presented. 3 crayons of different colours.

Procedure: Player connects the numbers as appropriate, using crayons.

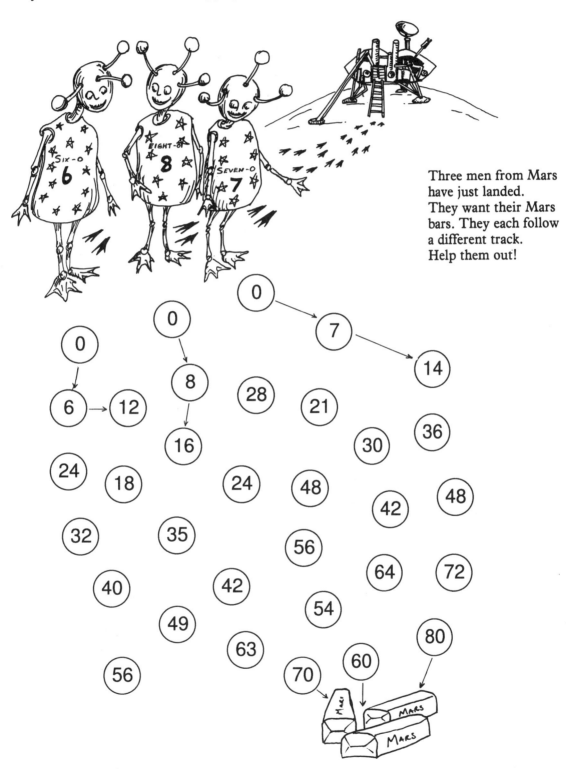

Three men from Mars
have just landed.
They want their Mars
bars. They each follow
a different track.
Help them out!

*Note
to teachers*   Of course, 24 occurs in the × 6 and × 8 series. 42 in × 6 and × 7, 48 in × 6 and × 8, and 56 in × 7 and × 8. It is of little consequence which 'track' the child takes; simply, when checking, remember different pupils' 'tracks' may not be identical, but still correct.

Game 100   Puzzle pics II

Objective: To identify products from 7 times table.

Number of participants: Individual.

Procedure: Colour all the numbers that can be divided by 7. What can you see there?

Pictures like these may use all four rules of number or any combination of them according to need.

Game 101   Factor freaks

Objective: To identify factors of numbers to 100.

Number of participants: Two, three or four.

Materials: Two packs of home-made (or printed) number cards. Pack 1 comprises 45 number cards: five of each number from 2 to 10. Pack 2 is made up of 32 single cards containing the numbers: 100, 90, 81, 80, 70, 64, 63, 60, 56, 54, 50, 49, 48, 45, 42, 40, 36, 35, 32, 30, 28, 27, 25, 24, 21, 20, 18, 16, 15, 14, 12, 10; table squares at first.

Procedure: Pack 1 is set out face up in nine piles of each number 2 to 10. Pack 2 is spread out face down over the table.

The first player turns over a card from pack 2 and tries to find two cards from the pack 1 piles that are factors of the first number. When he or she has done this the player retains the factor cards and returns the pack 2 card face down.

Each child takes a turn round the group until all the factor cards are used up. If there are no suitable factor cards left or the player doesn't spot them, he or she returns the card from pack 2 face down and the next player chooses a card.

The winner is the player whose factor cards give the highest total when added.

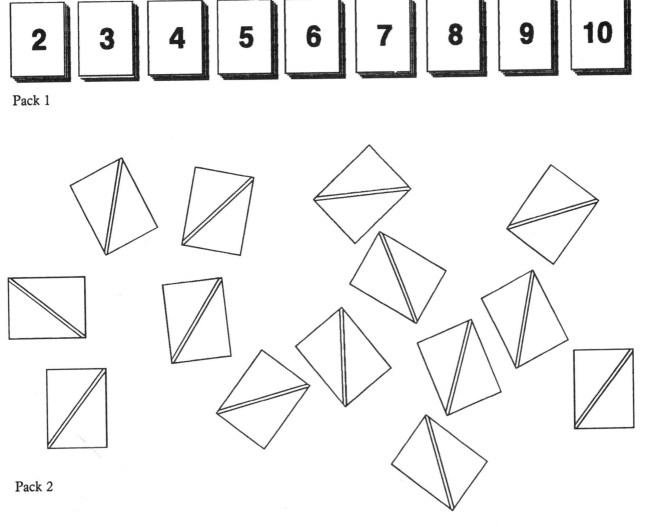

Pack 1

Pack 2

. . . etc. spread round the table face down.

Game 102   Funny things about 9

Objective: To illustrate a feature of the 9 times table.

Number of participants: One or a group.

Materials: Paper and pencil.

Procedure: Write out the × 9 table:

$$1 \times 9 = 9$$
$$2 \times 9 = 18$$
$$3 \times 9 = 27$$
$$4 \times 9 = 36$$
$$5 \times 9 = 45$$
$$6 \times 9 = 54$$
$$7 \times 9 = 63$$
$$8 \times 9 = 72$$
$$9 \times 9 = 81$$
$$10 \times 9 = 90$$

Look at the answers. Now, add the two figures you see for each answer. So, $1 + 8 = 9$. And $2 + 7 = 9$. Go on. Add the others all the way down. The answer is always...?

ANOTHER FUNNY THING USING 9

Objective: To practise subtraction and to use the 9 times table.

Number of participants: One or more, preferably a teenage group with various ages: no one younger than 12, or older than 19.

Materials: Paper and pencil.

Procedure: 'This is one definitely for the over-twelves!'

Write down your age.
  Reverse the figures.
    Subtract your age from the new number.
      Divide the answer by 9.
There will be no remainder.
There never will be for any age between, and including, 12 and 19.
Example:

You are, say, 14. Reverse 14	= 41
Subtract your age	− 14
	27

Divide your answer by 9   9)27
                                   3 exactly

Try it on your mates.'

This 'dodge' will work for many more numbers. Try exploring which ones with your pupils, and see if they can explain this phenomenon.

116

Game 103   Factors bingo

Objective: To practise tables up to 10 times 10.

Number of participants: Five players plus a caller.

Materials: A master card with 40 counters for the caller; five players' cards each with eight 'answers'.

40 counters/cardboard squares, eight per player; 40 counters for the caller; 100 tables flash cards each measuring 9 cm × 5 cm or larger. Each table requires 10 of these cards which can be used for other games as well as bingo.

3*	4*	5*	6*	7*	8*	9*	10*
12*	14*	15*	16*	18*	20*	21*	24*
25*	27*	28*	30*	32*	35*	36*	40*
42	45	48	49	50*	54	56	60
63	64	70	72	80	81	90	100

28	50	12	24	25
42		64		7

45	4	14	21	5
49		100		72

9	8	30	18	36
81		54		63

3	32	10	27	20
90		60		70

117

Procedure: Each player has a card and eight counters. The factor cards are shuffled and shown one at a time by the caller (factor side up). The answers can be printed on the backs of these cards for the caller to check. The players work out the problem displayed silently and the one with the answer on his or her card covers it with a counter.

Each factor is displayed once only and then put aside. The first player to cover all eight of his/her numbers correctly calls "Bingo!" or "House!" and is the winner.

Variation: For a quicker game the top line of the players' cards may be used. These are marked with an asterisk on the master card. Similarly the factor cards need to be marked and then, preferably, sorted before the abbreviated version is played.

BINGO PUZZLE: WHO CALLED 'BINGO!'?

These are the four cards in a game of bingo.

(1)

6	20		
	14		60
16		15	12

(2)

15			20
		21	6
18	16		50

(3)

21			6
14	15	12	
	50	16	

(4)

12		15	
		16	14
50		6	20

These are the factors that were shown by the caller.

| 5 x 4 | 2 x 3 | 3 x 5 | 7 x 2 | 4 x 3 | 4 x 4 | 5 x 10 |

Which player called 'Bingo!'?

118

Game 104 Four (five) in a line

Objective: Three games to provide tables practice with products to 100.

Number of participants: Two.

Materials: Tables square on card (as illustrated); coloured counters for each player (four each for the first game, five for the other two); a die for the first game, a spinner for the second, and a pair of dice for the third.

24 cm

Cover this section for younger players.

For Game 3

Game 1.
Procedure: The players roll the die for who starts, then roll it alternately. If, for example, 5 shows on the die the player may place one of his or her counters on any number that can be divided by 5, 10, 15 ... 50, or even to 100).

The second player might roll a 4. Then he or she may place a counter on any number divisible by 4.

Note: With young or slower players it is often helpful to cover the bottom four rows of the table square from 49, 56, 63 and 70 in this game, so that they can concentrate on finding "homes" for their counters in tables that stop at 10 × 6 and 6 × 10.

The winner is the player who gets a row of (horizontal) of four counters side by side, or a column (vertical) one above the other. So player 1, here, might eventually cover 5, 10, 15 and 20 first to win.

Game 2.   Use all the table square (up to 10 × 10) – if you haven't on *Game 1;* provide 5 counters each; and use a spinner as illustrated.

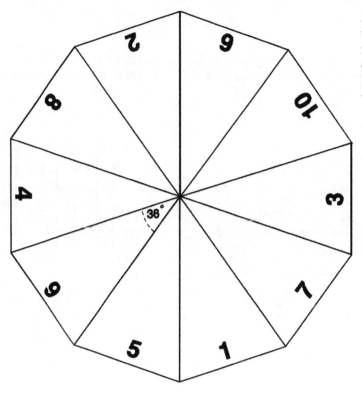

Make the spinner from thick card with a matchstick for the centre spindle. Fix the spindle with a spot of glue.

This time all the tables (to 10 × 10) are practised and five counters in a row or column are needed to win.

Game 3.   Provide an extended tables square to 12 × 12. Use two dice. Five adjacent counters again required to win.

Each player in turn rolls the dice, sums the resulting numbers and then covers any number on the square divisible by the total on the dice.

If orthodox (1 to 6) dice are used the × 6, × 7 (especially — why?) and × 8 tables will have a particularly good 'airing'.

In all three versions of this game the tables to be practised can be controlled by the labels on the dice or spinner. There is no need to stick to orthodox dice. Make one, perhaps, from a plain wooden cube with, say, 5 on two faces, 6 on another two and 7 on the remaining two.

Also, a spinner may also often be successfully 'loaded' by fixing a tiny piece of matchstick with sticky tape on the underside of the number you wish it to land on!

Game 105 Century

Objective: To practise addition bonds with totals from 2 to 12. To provide opportunities to distinguish between recognising + and × symbols.

Number of participants: Two or more.

Materials: One calculator for each participant. Two dice. One action plan (see below).

Procedure: Each player enters 1 into calculator. First player rolls two dice, mentally calculates his or her total score then applies the appropriate action from the plan on his calculator. Turns are taken until one player scores 100 or more to win.

Action Plan:

Total Score on Die	Action
7 or 11	× 2
5, 6, 8, 9	+ 2
2, 12	× 4
3, 4, 10	+ 4

Game 106 Shopping   Gamesheets 4 & 25

Objective: To practise addition bonds up to 100. To encourage mental addition.

Number of participants: Two or more.

Materials: Calculator for each player. Pack of cards numbered 1 – 9 for each player.

Card Number	Purchase
1	Pen
2	Crisps
3	Pencil
4	Notepad
5	Chocolate
6	Ruler
7	Biscuits
8	Rubber
9	Cola

Procedure: The cards should be combined and shuffled. Each player takes one card representing a purchase and enters the appropriate cost in the calculator. Further cards may be taken in turn and the costs added on. He or she may 'stick' when he or she draws a card which he or she realises would take the total beyond 100p (£1.00) so does not enter the value of this card onto the calculator.

The winner is the player nearest to £1.00 without exceeding it.

Variations: Change the price list. Alter the number of cards.

Game 107 99

Objective: To practise addition bonds. To provide an opportunity for logical thinking and realise a strategy is needed to win.

Number of participants: Two.

Materials: One calculator.

Procedure: First player enters any number between 1 and 10 on calculator.

Second player takes calculator and adds any number between 1 and 10. Repeat process. The first person to reach exactly 99 is the winner.

Strategy: Aim to be the first player to reach 11, 22, 33, 44, 55, 66, 77, 88 and thus 99.

Variation: Play as for game '99' but to win, reach total of 101.

Strategy: Aim to be the first player to reach 2, 13, 24, 35, 46, 57, 68, 79, 90 and thus 101.

Game 108   Air-sea-rescue   Gamesheet 26

Objectives: To provide opportunities to recognise size value and make comparisons.

Number of participants: Two.

Materials: Calculator. Two grids containing 9 × 9 squares. Two different coloured pencils.

Procedure: Following a disaster at sea, the pilot is to rescue as many people as possible.

Each player takes it in turn to enter each digit 1 — 9 in any order into each row of one grid. An exact copy is made on the second grid. Each player chooses flight path and marks it on own grid to rescue as many people as possible but the helicopter can only fly up to the next square or to the right of a pick-up. The maximum number of pick-ups is 17. The number of people rescued is added on the calculator. The winner is the pilot who rescued the most.

Example

Landing Base
↓

6	2	8	5	4	7	1	9	3
9	4	1	7	2	5	8	3	6
5	3	7	4	1	8	6	2	9
2	5	8	6	3	9	4	7	1
8	1	3	7	6	2	5	9	4
1	9	2	8	7	3	6	4	5
3	7	9	1	5	4	2	6	8
4	2	7	5	3	6	8	1	9
6	8	1	3	9	2	7	4	5

↑
Take Off Base

Possible Moves → or ↑

Number Rescued: 6 + 8 + 2 + 7 + 9 + 2 + 8 + 7 + 6 + 2 + 9 + 8 + 6 + 8 + 3 + 9 + 3 = 103

Game 109 Large as life!

Objective: To challenge pupils to develop strategies to make use of the calculator in reality situations involving large numbers.

Number of participants: Best carried out in pairs to facilitate discussion.

Note: Most problems will be best broken down, with an initial conceptual level within the pupils' grasp. One or more of the four basic operations must be selected — addition or multiplication in the examples given — making use of the calculator. Remember that the answer must be presented within the context of the original question.

How old am I?
How many months old am I
How many days old am I
How many hours old am I
How many minutes old am I

How many goals are scored each year in the 4 Football Leagues?

How many wooden blocks are there in the hall floor?

How many bricks were used to build the wall?

How much money to buy all the cars in the staff car park?

How many words are there in the story book?

Your local bus route is
. . . . . miles long.
There are . . . . . buses each day.
How many bus/miles are run each day?
In a month?
In a year?

Make up your own problems involving big numbers.

Estimate your answer before you use your calculator!

Place value: teaching for understanding from the beginning

1. When is a child ready for '10' and beyond?

Teachers must — as with smaller numbers — beware, a child's facility, or apparent facility, at counting. Often this is only a rote skill, and often does not indicate understanding.

2. Cardinality

The child should understand the cardinality (quantity) of the numbers 0 to 9. (Remember, teaching the nothingness of '0' often takes some time.) This understanding is demonstrated in three ways.

a. His or her *recognition of quantities:* his or her ability consistently to recognise, for example, a group (or set) of three objects from a collection of variously sized sets, and to know that the set is 'three' in response to "Show me the set of 'three' ".

b. The child should be able to *construct a set* to order. For example, he or she is able to make a set of five, or nine, or eight or whatever from a larger group of things.

c. The child should be able to *name a set*. When he or she is shown a set of seven objects, for example, he is able to tell you there are seven things on view.

So, first he or she must be able to recognise, construct and name any quantity from 0 to 9 using concrete objects.

3. Counting

A child should be able to count by rote (simply recite, parrot-like, the numbers in order) and count accurately any quantity of objects up to nine.

4. Symbols

He or she must know and always recognise all the symbols for 0 to 9. For example, on seeing the figure '6' he or she can name it 'six' consistently, without fail. These numerals can be connected with sets of objects. If the teacher gathers seven counters out of a pile, the child should be able to select a '7' (in plastic or on card) and place it by the selected group of counters. Similarly, if shown the figure '7', the child should pick out the 'seven' set from various sets of counters, beads or whatever.

The lack of understanding about '0' as a place holder in arithmetic bedevils computational accuracy. '0' first apears when one more is added to nine. The teaching of the how and why this occurs in our number system must be patient and well considered if years of frustration are to be avoided later.

5. Writing the symbols

The child should be able to write the numerals 0 to 9 when the teacher says them, in any order.

6. Introducing 10

a. This is best done with much practical experience of many groups of ten objects: from heaps of beads, plastic counters, buttons, pencils, toys and other handleable materials. Follow this with lots of work making groups of tens and ones accompanied by lots of talk about this process.

b. First use discontinuous materials, such as those mentioned above in (a), then gradually shift to continuous quantities by (i) threading the beads, buttons or washers, and then (ii) introducing Stern or Unifix material in 'tens', in which the 'ones' are clearly differentiated but not separate.

c. The third is to use strips of wood or cardboard ten Unifix blocks long with no 'ones' marked, or as long as a Stern 'ten' block. Cuisenaire or other unmarked materials are equally useful.

7. Abacuses and the first written recording of 10 +

a. The next step is to use a simple card-based abacus on which different coloured counters or building bricks represent tens and ones (say red for tens, blue for ones) when a set of objects is counted. Note that, as yet, the tens and ones are not always in columns; colour rather than position determines value.

b. Then follows the first, simple recording by placing the counters (or whatever) on a board marked in tens and ones with a dividing line vertically between them. Different colours for tens and ones are retained.

c. Objects identical in shape and colour are now used to keep tally, but in columns or trays; for example, dried peas or beads all the same colour on corrugate cardboard. Now only the position of the peas determines their cardinal value.

d. Next use this elementary abacus with the associated numerals. For example one pea in the ten column and six peas in the ones needs the numerals '16' in plastic or on card. The child writes it too.

e. Encourage transfer of learning by generalising this kind of work to various types of home-made and commercially produced abacuses.

The programme outlined above should take many months with most children. It might take years with slower children, but it should not be rushed. The temptation to move on to written sums quickly should be avoided!

Concrete materials and number lines are still of immense importance for children working with quantities as big as 100 and beyond. Generally, be slow to remove props of this nature.

Likewise, the importance of relating the skills of counting to 'real' contexts is paramount. For example, counting shoes in class, checking the number of books on the library shelf, counting the number for school dinner or moving outside for a traffic census with older juniors or secondary pupils varies the purpose of counting and applies the skill to acquiring useful information. Such simple, but genuine problems in school provide necessary practice and encourage understanding in depth of what happens when one or more is added to nine, or 99, or even 999 and beyond.

Gamesheets

Gamesheets are intended to be photocopied. Further instructions are to be found at the bottom of each sheet.

Game Number	Name	GAMESHEET number
8	Dotty dominoes	1a, b and c
16	Hanging to dry	2
19	Number series I	3
20	What's the number?	4
21	Got it! I	4
22	Matching pairs Stage 1	5a
	Matching pairs Stage 2	5b
	Matching pairs Stage 3	5c
23	10's in a Circle	6
25	Shapes to 10	7
30	Wheelies I	8
38	Got it! II	9
39	Chance	10
40	Pay up!	11
42	Making numbers	4
44	Got it! III	12
49	Make 11 (or 12 or 13 etc.)	13
52	Choose your number	4
56	Missing numbers II	14
61	Pairs	4 and 15
64	Building up	15
71	Pigeonholes	16
74	Fill the space	17
75	Digits	18
76	Three in a row	4
77	Keyboard snap	4
87	Wheelies II	8
88	Going for gold	19
91	Selection	4
92	Products	4
93	Multiples	20
94	Magic hexagons	21
96	Cover up	22
98	Tables snap	23
103	Factors bingo	24
106	Shopping	4 and 25
108	Air-sea rescue	26

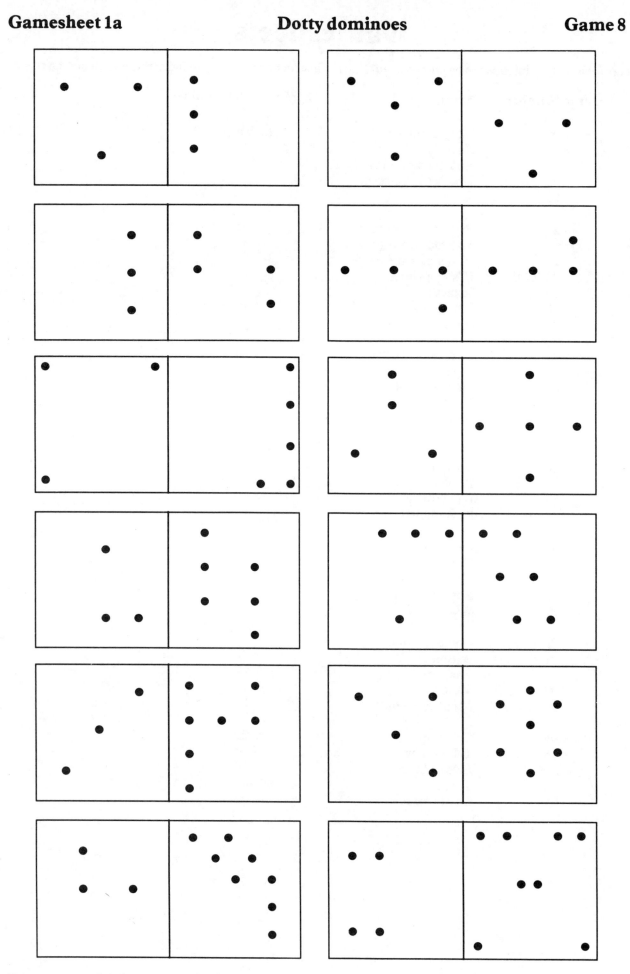

Paste on to card and cut out 12 dominoes.

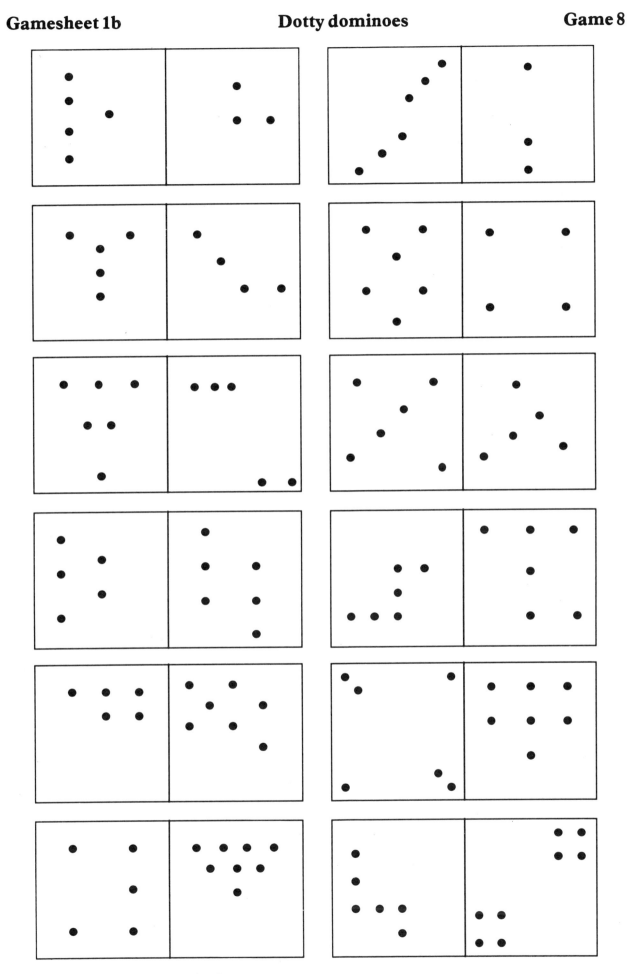

Paste on to card and cut out 12 dominoes.

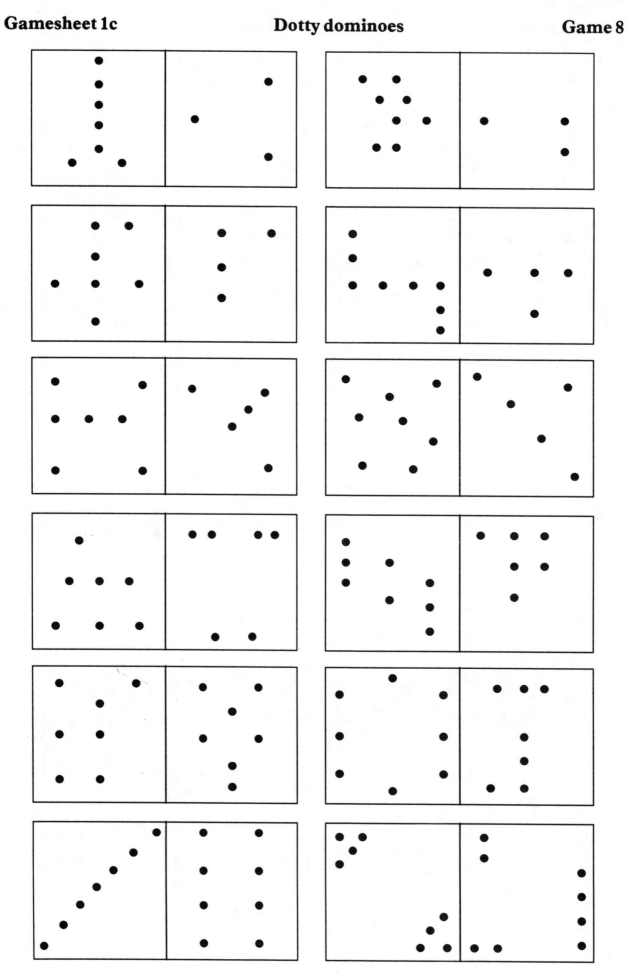

Paste on to card and cut out 12 dominoes.

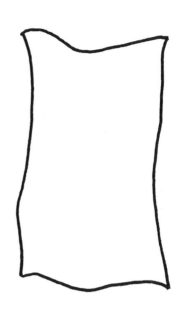

2 photocopies per game. Pupils colour clothes. Paste on to card and cut out.

Join up the numbers. Start with the *smallest*. End with the *biggest*. use arrows.

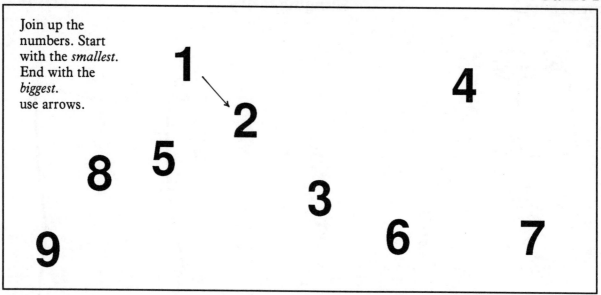

Join up the numbers. Start with the *biggest*. End with the *smallest*. use arrows.

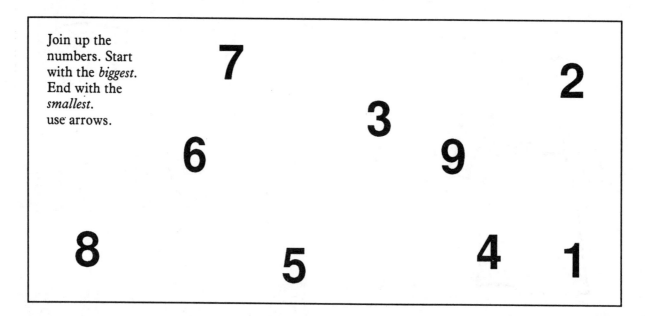

Join up the *even* numbers. Start with the *smallest*.

Join up the *odd* numbers. Start with the *biggest*. Use arrows.

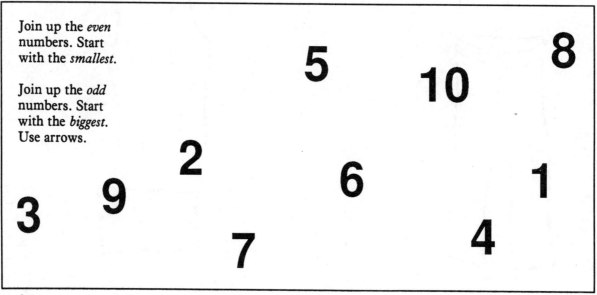

Use photocopy as worksheet.

1	**2**	**3**
4	**5**	**6**
7	**8**	**9**
0	Paste on to card and cut out numbers. Cover with plastic film.	

Paste on to card. Cut along double lines to make dominoes.

Paste on to card. Cut along double lines to make dominoes.

6	1	2	3	4	5	
5	6	6	6	6	6	
5	6	1	2	3	4	5
4	4	5	5	5	5	5
4	5	6	1	2	3	4
3	3	3	4	4	4	4
3	4	5	6	1	2	3
2	2	2	2	3	3	3
2	3	4	5	6	1	2
1	1	1	1	1	2	2

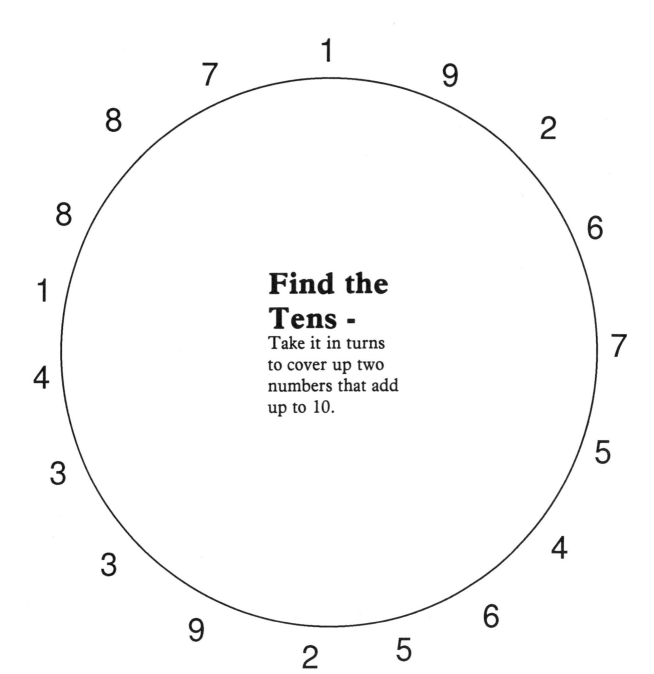

Find the Tens -
Take it in turns to cover up two numbers that add up to 10.

Use photocopy as worksheet.

Example 1.

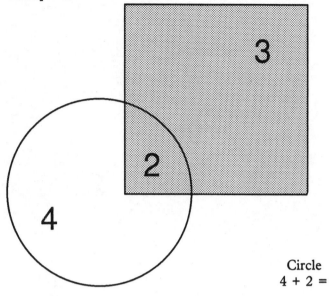

Circle　　　　　Square
4 + 2 =　　　　2 + 3 =

Example 2.

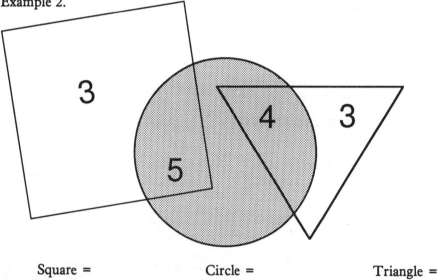

Square =　　　　　Circle =　　　　　Triangle =

Example 3.

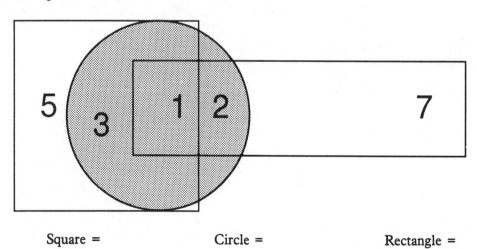

Square =　　　　　Circle =　　　　　Rectangle =

Use photocopy as worksheet.

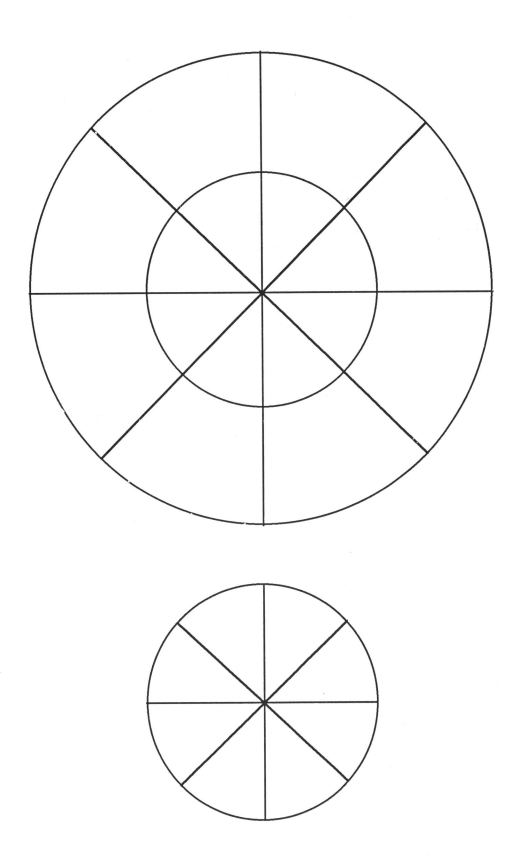

Paste on to card, cut out and insert symbols according to requirements.

1	2	3	4	5	6	7	8	9	10
11	12	13	14	15	16	17	18	19	20
21	22	23	24	25	26	27	28	29	30
31	32	33	34	35	36	37	38	39	40
41	42	43	44	45	46	47	48	49	50
51	52	53	54	55	56	57	58	59	60
61	62	63	64	65	66	67	68	69	70
71	72	73	74	75	76	77	78	79	80
81	82	83	84	85	86	87	88	89	90
91	92	93	94	95	96	97	98	99	100

Use photocopy as worksheet.

Paste on to card. Cover with plastic film.

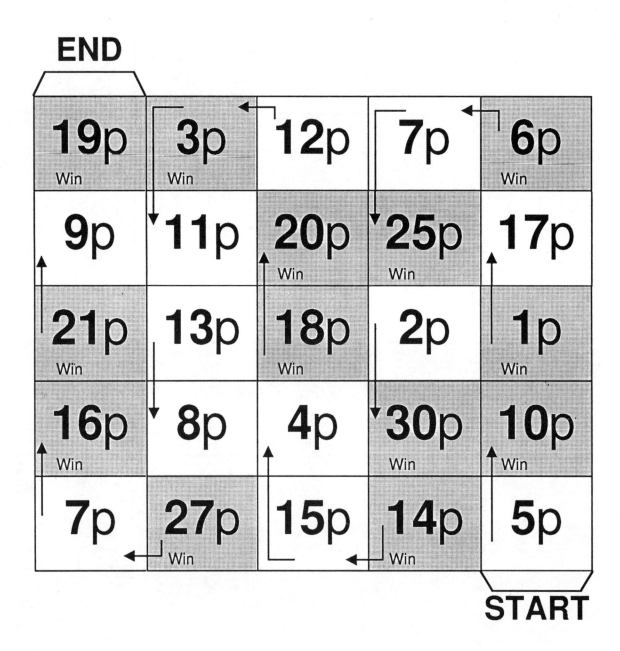

Paste on to card. Cover with plastic film.

3 ones	2 ones	1 one	0 ones
11 ones	10 ones	5 ones	4 ones
5 tens	4 tens	3 tens	12 ones
43 tens	42 tens	41 tens	40 tens
5 hundreds	3 hundreds	51 tens	45 tens

Paste on to card and cut out.

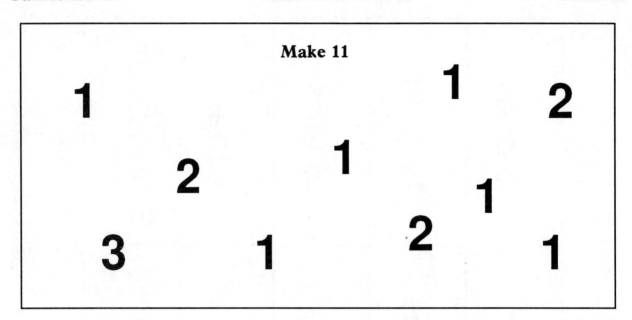

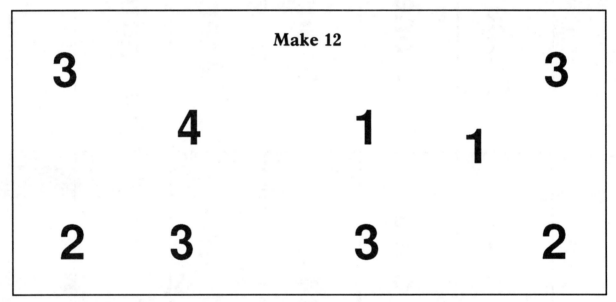

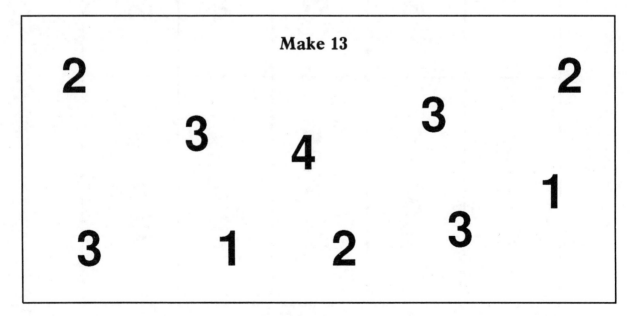

Paste on to card and cut out. Cover with plastic film.

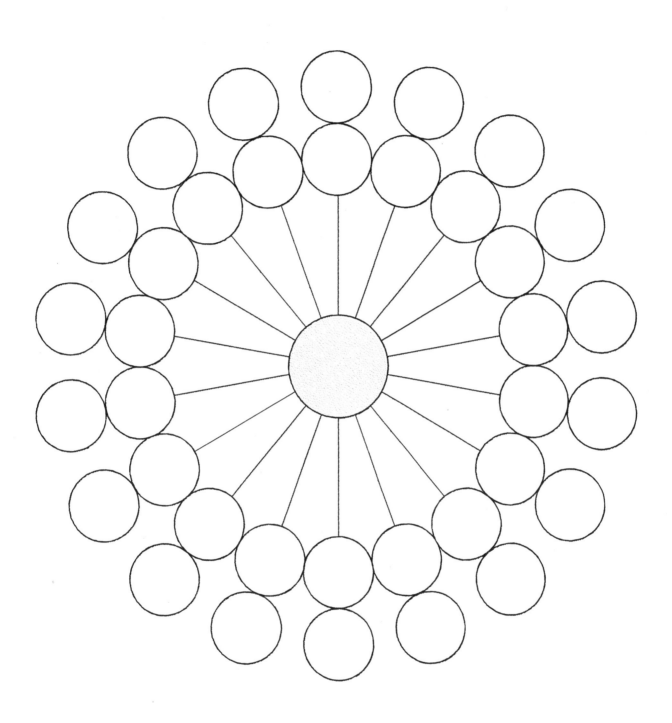

Photocopy one for each number required from 10 to 19. Paste on to card.
Fill in number (from 10 to 19) in centre circle.
Insert numbers as appropriate in the outer ring of circles.

10	**11**	**12**
13	**14**	**15**
16	**17**	**18**
19	**20**	

Paste on to card and cut out numbers. Cover with plastic film. Use Gamesheet 4 for 1 to 9.

primary number ↓		odd number ↓		multiple of 3 ↓	
					← factors of 12
					← even numbers
					← multiples of 5

1	2	3	4	5	6	7
8	9	10	11	12	13	14
15	16	17	18	19	20	21
22	23	24	25	26	27	28
29	30					

Paste PIGEONHOLE board on to card. Cover with plastic film. Paste numbers on to card and cut out.

20 = 5 4	20 - 5 =	4 = 16 4	19 = + 11	7 x = 14	17 9 = 8
8 + = 19	14 - = 10	÷ 2 = 9	5 3 = 15	6 = 18 3	1 11 = 11
20 - = 11	7 + = 9	x 6 = 18	11 8 = 19	12 ÷ 2 =	5 = 16 11

Paste on to card and cut out.

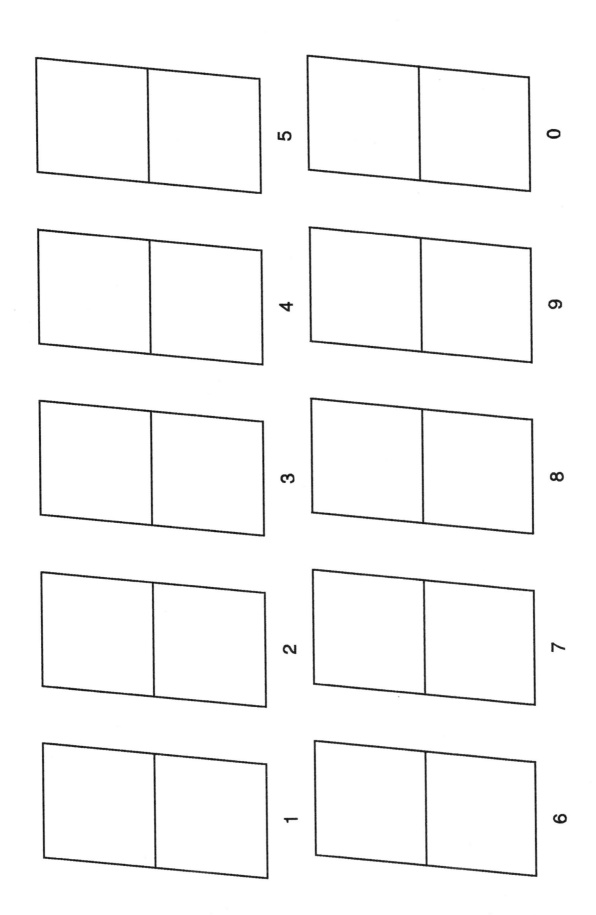

Use photocopy as worksheet.

6	1	16	5
9	gold	4	11
gold	18	gold	8
0	gold	10	12
3	7	2	15

Paste on to card. Cover with plastic film.

400 x 2	20 x 40	40 x 20	
2 x 400	200 x 4	4 x 200	
4 x 2	2 x 4	4 x 20	2 x 40

Paste on to card and cut out.

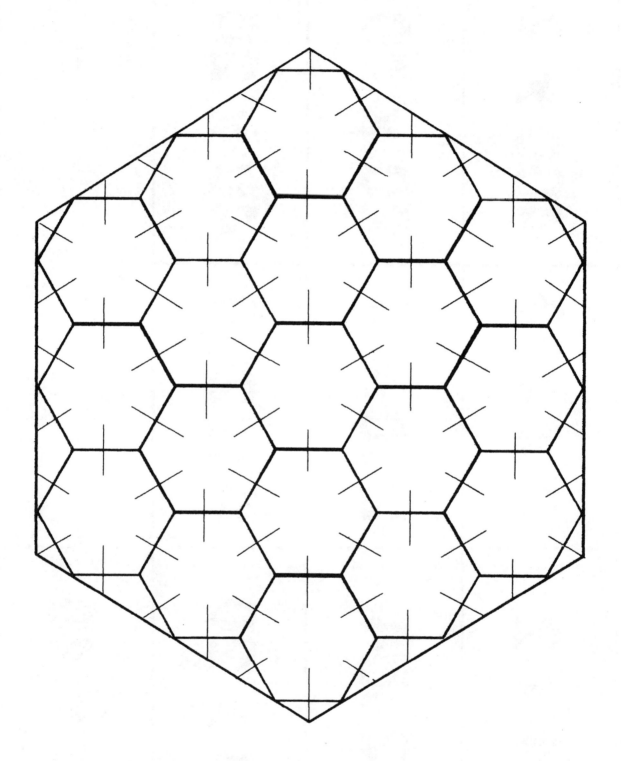

Paste on to card. Cover with plastic film.

3	6	10	16	24	36
2	5	9	15	20	30
1	4	8	12	18	25
		7	11		

	7	11			
3	6	10	16	24	36
2	5	9	15	20	30
1	4	8	12	18	25

Paste on to card. Cover with plastic film.

Paste on to card and cut out. 'Fact' and 'Answer' cards are completed according to the table being practised.

MASTER CARD

3*	4*	5*	6*	7*	8*	9*	10*
12*	14*	15*	16*	17*	18*	20*	24*
25*	27*	28*	30*	32*	35*	36*	40*
42	45	48	49	50*	54	56	60
63	64	70	72	80	81	90	100

BLANKS FOR PLAYERS CARDS

Paste Master Card on to card and cover with plastic film. Fill in numbers as required on players cards. Paste on to card.

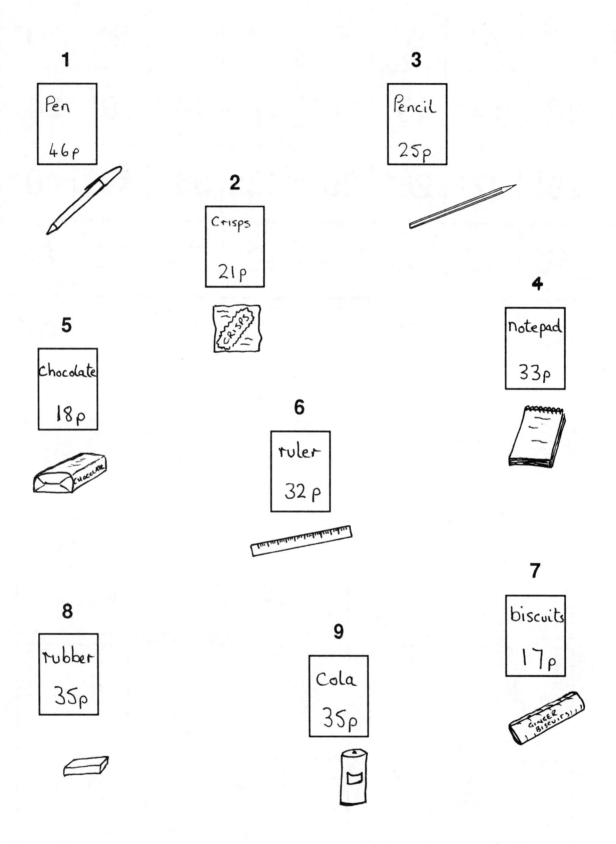

1

Pen

46p

3

Pencil

25p

2

Crisps

21p

5

Chocolate

18p

4

Notepad

33p

6

ruler

32p

7

biscuits

17p

8

rubber

35p

9

Cola

35p

Use photocopy as worksheet.

6	2	8	5	4	7	1	9	3
9	4	1	7	2	5	8	3	6
5	3	7	4	1	8	6	2	9
2	5	8	6	3	9	4	7	1
8	1	3	7	6	2	5	9	4
1	9	2	8	7	3	6	4	5
3	7	9	1	5	4	2	6	8
4	2	7	5	3	6	8	1	9
6	8	1	3	9	2	7	4	5

↑
Take Off Base

Use photocopy as worksheet.